# From Little Acorns

# From Little Acorns

A History of The A.P.V. Company Limited

G. A. DUMMETT
M.A., F.Eng., F.I.Chem.E.

Hutchinson Benham
*London*

Hutchinson Benham Limited
3 Fitzroy Square, London W1P 6JD

An imprint of the Hutchinson Group

London Sydney Melbourne Auckland
Wellington Johannesburg and agencies
throughout the world

First published 1981
© The A.P.V. Company Limited

Set in 11pt Souvenir Light by
V & M Graphics Ltd, Aylesbury, Bucks.
Printed and bound by
R. J. Acford

ISBN 0 09 146370 X

# Contents

# List of Illustrations

# Foreword

This book is written for the many friends of the APV Company and in appreciation of the contribution made by so many of its employees past and present. It serves as a record of achievement of a company now part of a much larger group. The other group companies also have long and interesting histories and may one day be the subject of similar review.

Not many companies have a founder working actively in the business for sixty-two years, particularly in this century and in a company where high technology has been the road to success.

This story takes us to 1977 when my predecessor, Sir Peter Seligman, son of the founder, retired as Chairman of the company. The author, Mr G. A. Dummett, retired in 1972 after thirty-seven years' service, for sixteen of which he was an Executive Director. During most of his service he was concerned with research and development and therefore worked in close contact with Dr Seligman for many years. Mr Dummett was also able to call on the experiences of other long-service personnel who had in the past direct communication with those who worked in the company from the beginning.

I hope that the book will make interesting reading for our many friends. For students of social and technical history it will provide evidence of an enterprise founded on the skills of one man, the strength and ability of one family leading to a public company and an industrial group that has never forgotten its origins in good applied science, and the need to offer a service to the industries it serves.

H. P. N. Benson
*Executive Chairman*
*A.P.V. Holdings Limited*

# Preface

This is a history of The A.P.V. Company Limited. In itself that statement calls for some explanation. 'APV' in the City or the pages of the financial press means APV Holdings, a large group of technological companies and a world leader in its field. So why is this not a history of APV Holdings?

There are two main reasons. Firstly, it would be too complicated for a coherent story. There are some seventy subsidiary or associated companies of APV Holdings in more than twenty countries. Of these, about a dozen have interesting histories of their own which could not reasonably be ignored.

Secondly, until 1962 the APV Company and its subsidiaries was the group. Only then, when a major series of acquisitions and mergers started, did it become less than the dominant member of the group. By that time the pattern for future development had been established. It seemed more profitable and interesting to trace the story of the single company from the little acorn planted by Richard Seligman in an old maltings in a back street in Wandsworth to the Sussex oak of the big Crawley establishment, and only incidentally refer to the world-wide holdings company.

I must emphasise that this is very much 'a' history. Any such account has to try to unravel the interwoven strands of personalities, of technological development, of production and of commerce and finance. It is no coincidence, for example, that the story falls into quite well-defined sections corresponding to successive technological developments and that these coincide with major changes of personnel whether of Chairman, Chief Engineer or Works Manager.

Nor is it surprising that finance played an increasingly dominant part in the growth of the company as it steadily expanded. Where APV can count itself fortunate is in having had a Board that could appreciate the need for new blood in a crisis and could find the right men at the right time.

Anyone trying to disentangle these threads will have to discard a great mass of not insignificant fact. In making a selection, he will be influenced by his own view of the company. Mine is coloured by my experience of it, in technology, in marketing and in the Boardroom. Such distortion as may result is entirely my responsibility.

There is one form of distortion, however, that I have been at some pains to avoid. While this story is one of almost continuous growth over two-thirds of a century, it is not without its ups and downs.

But the qualities of a company and those who work for it are seen at their best in times of trouble, not when success is coming easily. I have therefore tried not to gloss over difficulties, whether financial or technical, in the Boardroom, in the works or in the market place, for it is how these difficulties are met that reveals the true strength of a company.

In trying to expose the various strands that form the skein of this history, I have been struck by several basic and repeating threads.

First, the overwhelming importance of innovation, the marriage of a perceived market need to a solution of the technological problem posed. It is a process involving entrepreneurial as well as inventive ability. As on several occasions in this history, it may even involve superseding successful earlier developments in order to meet changing conditions.

Then, the value of basing an engineering business on a relatively restricted range of products that can be sold in a wide variety of industries and developing an organisation to market them all over the globe. As a result the APV Company's trade has been relatively well cushioned against fluctuations in its various markets.

Finally, the importance of sound, common-sense, financial management. As this history shows, the margin between commercial failure and success is often surprisingly small. Without it, no innovation, however inspired, will in the long run succeed.

The history of a company, however, must ultimately be that of its people. Most contribute simply by loyally carrying out their day-to-day jobs, on the shop floor or in the offices; many play a more influential role through the business and social operations of the firm; while only a few are able to play a decisive part in management. The success of the company is due to them all, men and women alike. It is regrettable, therefore, that so few can be mentioned by name from the many gifted craftsmen, engineers, salesmen and others.

Equally, many episodes that those who knew the company well will remember, have had to be discarded. On the other hand, every essential statement in this chronicle is based on documentary evidence, though a lot of this is patchy; for instance, much earlier information on sales and staff has not survived and wartime records were of necessity restricted.

Nevertheless, there has been a lot to draw on. Annual reports and chairmen's statements are freely available. So are APV brochures, patents and other publications of which the house journals, particularly the APV *Bulletin* (1946–1957) and *News* (1958–1977) have proved particularly valuable.

In addition, I have had access to Board minutes and confidential papers as well as such early notebooks and ledgers as exist. Even more valuable, I have been able to consult many of Richard Seligman's papers and letters to his family from school and university, to Moritz, first Chairman of the company, and to J. W. Wilson, his colleague as joint Managing Director.

I am most grateful to the company for making so much available to me and allowing me a free hand with it.

I am also indebted to all those old colleagues who have helped with friendly criticism and reminiscence. If I mention David Shore, Managing Director of the APV Company, in particular, it is because the idea of producing a history of the firm first stemmed from him.

Finally, my special thanks are due to Valerie Higgs without whose brilliant secretarial talents this book could never have been produced.

# Chapter 1
# Background

The Aluminium Plant and Vessel Company Limited, the forerunner of The A.P.V. Company Limited and A.P.V. Holdings Limited, was given its Certificate of Incorporation on 10 June and the first meeting of directors was held on 20 June 1910.

These date the founding of the company. But before recounting its evolution from that point, it is necessary to look back, partly because the factors that led up to its foundation were complex and affected its future development but even more because the character and outlook of its founder, Doctor Richard Seligman, was to dominate the company over the first forty years or so of its existence.

Richard Joseph Simon Seligman was born on 17 March, Saint Patrick's day, 1878, the son of Isaac and Lina Seligman. Isaac was a member of the great banking family of Seligman that originated from Baiersfeld in Bavaria whence eight brothers, including Isaac, the youngest, and three sisters, emigrated to the United States between 1837 and 1843, to be followed soon after by their father, David. This was no wealthy exodus. They crossed the Atlantic steerage in sailing vessels but, once arrived, the family developed its banking interests to such an extent that it played a prominent part in financing Abraham Lincoln.

The firm of Seligman Brothers was founded in New York under two of the brothers and further pairs of brothers were despatched to London, Paris and Frankfurt to found similar banking establishments there. Isaac, with his brother Leopold, came to

1

London and founded the firm of Seligman Brothers that exists to this day incorporated in S. W. Warburg and Company Limited. Both of them were destined to play an important part in the development of the APV Company later on.

Richard Seligman's mother, Lina, was born into a Darmstadt banking firm, the elder sister of Rudolph Messel F.R.S. who developed the contact process for sulphuric acid at the Silvertown works of the company that became Spencer, Chapman and Messel Limited.

Richard was therefore born into a family strongly entrepreneurial on both sides and with direct links to the relatively new and rapidly developing chemical industry. It was quite international in outlook. His family environment was a close-knit, loving, lively and cultivated one where both sport and the arts were valued and practised. The family was a large one, four sons, Charles, Hugo, Richard and Gerald, and three daughters.

The house where he was born, Lincoln House in Clapham Park, reflected the prosperity and standing of the family. It was called after Isaac Seligman's great hero, Abraham Lincoln, and had been built for his personal use by Thomas Cubitt, the superb speculative builder of Belgravia. Advertising the house for sale in 1870, it is described as an 'exceptionally compact residential property'. This is hardly how it would be described today. Eighteen bedrooms, but only two bathrooms, stabling for six horses and five carriages, cow house for three cows, dairy, laundry, vineyard, melon ground and every conceivable sort of room, outhouse and equipment, including central heating, were enclosed by over twenty-two acres of grounds and all within four miles of Charing Cross. Sadly it is impossible now to recognise the site of this splendid estate amid the villas, blocks of flats and maisonettes that now constitute Clapham Park.

Richard grew up in these happy and patrician surroundings until, after a couple of years at a private school, he passed into Harrow.

At Harrow he was put on the classical side. From his letters to his mother it is apparent that this was a mistake. He found the work very hard and unrewarding and, as a result, never made the progress that he and his parents felt he should. When it was realised that he would have done far better on the modern side, it was too late to make the change, so in December 1894 he left school when he was still not yet seventeen.

Just before that he had written to his mother, 'I have quite made up my mind that engineering or chemical work is the profession I would like.' By the time he left Harrow, the die was cast. He was to enter the Central Technical College of the City and Guilds Institute in London (now incorporated in Imperial College) to read engineering. However, when he passed the entrance examination, he found he had put his name down on the wrong list and had been accepted for the chemical and not the engineering department as he had intended.

Richard remained at the Central College until 1898 when he passed out with the Associateship of the City and Guilds Institute (transmuted to a Fellowship in 1937). During this time he came under the influence of the great H. E. Armstrong who was then professor of chemistry, an inspiring teacher but one whose ideas of physical chemistry were unusual to put it mildly. As a result, Seligman's physical chemical theory and, with it, chemical engineering were always distinctly shaky. But he imbibed from Armstrong an enthusiasm for science and its application. He developed under him an open mind to the trends of technological development and a willingness to accept and act on the results of scientific experiment even when they were unpalatable.

After leaving the Central College he decided, urged on by Armstrong, to continue his academic studies and take a doctorate. Germany was the obvious place to go and so, towards the end of 1898, he entered the ancient University of Heidelberg, living with his dog in lodgings up the hill near the castle overlooking the valley of the Neckar and the old town.

For some reason, he took the unusual course of starting his chemical studies at the beginning again. He also read physics, mineralogy, botany and geology. He found the work comparatively easy but the hours worked were another matter. A typical timetable, he wrote, would include lectures and laboratory work from 7.15 a.m. to 1 p.m. and after lunch from 2 p.m. to 6 p.m.; tennis or rowing from 6.15 p.m. to 8 p.m.; and work again from 9 to 10.30 in the evening. Saturday's work stopped at 4 p.m. and on Sundays his hours were only from 9 a.m. to 12.30 p.m. Even allowing for a young man's exaggeration, it is clear that he was working very hard.

But he was by no means just a bookworm. Even when he was still at Harrow and winter sports were practically unknown, he went on visits to Mürren and Grindelwald. He was one of the earliest British skiers. He introduced skis from Norway into Switzerland and he continued to be a keen skier for another thirty or forty years after. He was an active rambler and fell walker, especially in connection with his botanical and geological interests, until well into his late seventies. What is less to be expected by those who knew him only in later life was his enjoyment of squash and tennis (he won the men's doubles at Heidelberg), rowing, swimming, riding, grouse and pheasant shooting and even stag hunting.

The pattern of his interests in later life had already been established. He had a deep interest in everything scientific and technological with a typically nineteenth-century belief in their powers, but also a liberal conviction that they were only valuable insofar as they could be devoted to the public good. He applied his scientific knowledge to his outside hobbies, at first geology but more and more in later years alpine botany in which he became an acknowledged authority. Finally, there was his devotion to his family, the Seligmans and all who were related to them.

During his second year at Heidelberg, he began to find the familiar chemical work dull so he decided to break off his work at Heidelberg and find a place in Bamberger's laboratory in the Federal Technical High School in Zürich where he could undertake research in organic chemistry as the basis for a thesis to present for his doctorate. Towards the end of 1900 he started work in Zürich. He had hoped that he might be able to take his doctorate in 1901 but was advised that this length of study was insufficient and so

4

he stayed on to work under Bamberger at Zürich for a second year.

Another circumstance was making him not unwilling to stay on in Zürich. He had met a beautiful and talented girl, Hilda MacDowell, daughter of an Irish sculptor living in England. She was spending a year in Zürich and they must have seen a lot of each other. Both families, however, were opposed to a union, so it was not until Richard was independent that they were able to get married. That was in September 1906. They had a daughter and four sons, two of whom eventually joined the APV Company.

The Technical High School in Zürich was not then qualified to confer doctorates; this had to be done by a university. Seligman, therefore, had to consider where he would present his thesis. At the end of May 1902 he left for Heidelberg where, feeling some trepidation, he was examined at the end of July and the following day was awarded his Doctor of Philosophy *summa cum laude*, the equivalent of our first class.

He was greatly pleased – a facsimile of his degree certificate hung on the wall of his study at APV until the day of his death – and so, too, was his family. There is no doubt that he felt that this had justified the support his parents had given him for over seven years since leaving school.

In November, he returned to Zürich to wind up his research there and prepare it for publication. But now that he was qualified, he found life in a university laboratory irksome and wanted to 'work in earnest for some definite purpose'.

But what was his career to be? He had rebelled against becoming the 'hands attached to Bamberger's (or anyone else's) brain', so he rejected Armstrong's proposal to work with him. Eventually it was decided that he should visit the United States but should try and get some industrial experience before he left.

So, when he returned to England in early 1903, he secured a post as volunteer in the laboratory of the British Uralite Company Limited at Higham in Kent, makers of a silicate-bonded asbestos building material. Here he worked under Percy Williams who was in charge of the laboratory. So began a friendship that lasted until

Williams' death in 1942, a friendship that was very fruitful for the Aluminium Plant and Vessel Company of which he was to be Chief Chemist for twenty-eight years.

Seligman lived on the works, a desolate spot close to the Thames. As there was nothing else to do he spent his evenings stoking boilers, working gas producers or running different parts of the plant, practical industrial experience that was to stand him well in later life.

Early in the autumn of that year he was introduced to Bonner, the Chairman of the British Aluminium Company, a fateful encounter that was to have a decisive effect on Seligman's career. He suggested that Seligman should join William Mills, aluminium founders in Sunderland, and put some money into the business. It was accordingly arranged that he should use his forthcoming visit to America to acquire such knowledge as he could about aluminium. He anticipated entering the aluminium industry in the near future.

He left in autumn 1903 and spent a very busy ten weeks in New York, visiting factories, university laboratories and industrial personalities, and collaborating in the development of copper-impregnated packing papers.

At the end of the year, he was shocked to learn that the arrangement for his participation in William Mills' foundry business was not going to materialise; from now on he had to make his own way in the world.

Some time before, Dr Waldstein, with whom he had been working on copper salts, had suggested a scheme for brominating pentane under the influence of radiation as a step in the production of amyl alcohol. It was proposed that Seligman should work this out in the Niagara Research Laboratories, a small privately run concern. He accepted the offer and left for Niagara Falls in January 1904.

He started work in the middle of February and his work went so well that after three weeks he was taken on the staff at $100 a month (about £250 per annum), not a bad starting salary in those days. Between then and the middle of June he produced four reports of work that in essence established the basis of an industrial process.

While he was in New York he had met a member of the family of Guggenheim Brothers that owned a number of large metallurgical plants. As a result, in July 1904, Seligman was appointed Chief Chemist to the United States Zinc Company of Pueblo, Colorado, one of their great smelting companies. Thus started an active interest in the metallurgical industries that was to continue until the end of his life.

By the end of the month he was established in his new job at the smelting plant at Blend some miles out of Pueblo on the prairie. Here he lived at the works, sharing a two-roomed hut with a workman and his wife. Just as at British Uralite, when he had finished in the laboratory he went down to the works to watch or help in the operation of the furnaces. This first-hand experience of the living and working conditions of his workforce, so different from the well-to-do surroundings in which he was brought up, gave him an unusual sympathy with his shopfloor workpeople that was to stand him in good stead later.

His work was concerned largely with routine chemical analysis. This was quite unfamiliar to him so that he found it very hard and exhausting. There was no question of research being undertaken at Blend, so he left at the end of the year to take up an offer from British Aluminium to become their first Research Chemist at Milton in Staffordshire.

British Aluminium at that time possessed only rudimentary control laboratories for its seven production plants and carried out no research. Seligman therefore had virtually a virgin field to develop. At first his work was mainly concerned with methods of analysis and the setting up of new laboratories at Milton and the other works. In August 1907 he was made Chief Chemist to the company responsible for all chemical, metallurgical and electro-chemical processes throughout the company.

There followed a series of investigations on a variety of subjects including several on the electro-chemical manufacture of aluminium from bauxite that resulted in great economic benefits to the company.

But the most significant task assigned to him and the most important in its consequences was to investigate methods of joining aluminium. At the time the only method available was riveting and this was quite unsatisfactory both mechanically and as a cause of corrosion.

He first attempted to find a suitable solder and examined all those known. He soon came to the quite correct conclusion that on theoretical grounds alone these experiments were doomed to failure.

He therefore turned his attention to autogenous welding. But here the difficulty was that aluminium, even when molten, forms a skin of refractory oxide that effectively prevents fusion between the base and the weld metal taking place. In alumina reduction furnaces this difficulty is overcome by melting under a flux that dissolves alumina to form a fluid protective layer on the surface of the metal. Seligman had the idea of using a similar flux in the welding process and started experiments with various mixtures of alkali chlorides and fluorides to obtain a mixture of the right melting point, density and solvent power for alumina.

There is little doubt that this work would have been completely successful but, before he had gone far, he received some samples of welded joints that showed that the problem had already been solved on the continent. A little later the patents, in the name of a Dutchman named Schoop, reached him and proved that the process was exactly as he had foreseen.

He at once reported back to his head office and urged that the British rights be acquired but was met with scepticism. It was even suggested that he had been hoodwinked. Seligman was pained but let the matter drop as far as British Aluminium were concerned.

Towards the end of 1908, however, the company was running into financial difficulties and it had become clear that it would not be possible to give him the resources for research that he had been led to expect would be put at his disposal. He accordingly applied for release from his engagement with the company and left at the end of the year. There can be little doubt that this was something of a relief to him; he wrote at the time of 'regaining his freedom'. He always felt at his best when he was his own master.

Already he had an eye on the Schoop process, the patent rights for which had been taken over by the A. G. für Autogene Aluminium Schweissung (Autogenous Aluminium Welding Company) of Zürich. No move was made immediately for he could not clearly envisage a suitable commercial application although he was aware in general terms of the possible use of aluminium in breweries.

At this point, Seligman had a remarkable stroke of luck. In the spring of 1909, he had to undertake a journey to Germany. In the train between Cologne and Berlin he happened to share a compartment with an elderly gentleman with whom he fell into conversation. This proved to be Dr E. R. Moritz, one of the foremost British brewery consultants. He revealed a considerable interest in the use of aluminium as a material of construction for brewery tanks, particularly conditioning vessels, but could not follow it up as he knew of no satisfactory method of fabrication. Seligman then told him that he believed he knew of someone who could produce suitable vessels and it was agreed that if some could be obtained, Moritz would undertake tests in his laboratory. Thus started a close association that lasted until Moritz' death.

A couple of small vessels were obtained straight away from Autogene Aluminium Schweissung (AAS) in Zürich, one a small two-litre pressure vessel and the other an oak fermenting vessel of the same size lined with aluminium. Within a month, they were under test and by the last week in July, Moritz reported that the tests were satisfactory as far as solution of aluminium was concerned and a month later that the fermentation test had gone successfully. It was decided to proceed to a larger scale.

But before this was done, Seligman approached AAS in Zürich and acquired for himself the British rights to the Schoop process under an agency arrangement. He set up an office and laboratory where he was joined by A. V. Hussey and A. Winlo, his first employees in the new venture, and they started the production of welding flux, experimental welding and investigations on applications of welded plant.

In the course of a visit to Zürich in September, Seligman reported on the very satisfactory performance of a welded aluminium fermenting vessel in a Swiss brewery. Armed with this information, Moritz approached Fuller, Smith and Turner at Chiswick, and at the beginning of October reported that the managing director, H. F. Fuller, had agreed to have a small fermenting vessel lined with aluminium on sale or return. A two-barrel conditioning vessel was obtained from Zürich and a fifty-barrel fermenting vessel was lined by Fässler, one of AAS's welders, sent over to work under Seligman's direction (Illustration 2). For this the Swiss company were paid £50. The fermenting vessel remained in service for over fifty years. Both vessels were completely successful and it became apparent from the attitude of a number of brewers that the welding process could have a considerable future.

To exploit it satisfactorily would clearly involve manufacture in this country and this would mean establishing a company to do so. By February 1910, this was already under discussion between Seligman and Moritz. Moritz was not prepared to invest any capital in the new company but he agreed to serve on the Board and to give his services for a share in the profits. In the upshot it was agreed that a new £5,000 company should be established with Moritz as Chairman, and Seligman as Managing Director. Subsequently Moritz suggested that H. F. Fuller should join the Board.

Having got so far, the first essential was to arrange the terms of a licence with AAS in Zürich. The negotiations were protracted and were not concluded until July. The terms of the agreement appear to have covered all industries for a royalty equal to 25% of the profit, with a minimum royalty of £200 p.a. and with AAS undertaking to maintain the patents.

While all this was going on, more work was being sought, mainly in breweries in and around London. Russell's Gravesend brewery provided the first work for the new company, an order for a fifty-barrel conditioning vessel.

It was at this point, in April 1910, that Seligman made the first rough estimate of what resources would be required. He envisaged that the first year's production would consist of:

12 large (ninety-barrel) low-pressure conditioning vessels
28 small (fifteen-barrel) high-pressure conditioning vessels
60 small linings (e.g. five-barrel yeast waggons)
35 larger linings (e.g. forty-barrel stout tanks)
30 large (sixty-barrel) fermenting vessels.

Assuming labour costs of 8*d* an hour (3.3p) and an oncost of 1s1*d* an hour (5.4p) with material at just over a shilling (5p) a pound and profit of 25% on selling price, he calculated that this would give a turnover of about £7,000.

He assumed a workforce of ten men working 2,750 hours a year, equivalent to 55 hours a week with no holidays but bank holidays, at a wage of £1 16s 8*d* (£1.83) per week.

The rest of the staff were assessed as:

Manager – £200 per annum
Foreman – £200 per annum if he came from Switzerland, or
          £100 per annum if he were a 'working' foreman
Chemist – £200 per annum including laboratory expenses
Three or four clerks, etc. – £200 per annum the lot

Thus, including Seligman himself, there would be a staff of seven or eight. The total expenses were estimated at £1,500 including staff salaries. It is not surprising that these estimates were to prove highly optimistic.

He reckoned that the accommodation needed immediately would be:

ground-floor shop about 100 ft × 40 ft
with another about 20 ft × 30 ft
store room
3 office rooms
laboratory
yard space

with another main shop of similar size (4,000 square feet) being needed before the end of the year if the business were successful.

It was essential at this stage to find a manager and send him to Zürich for training. By the end of April he had engaged J. Gallon, at a salary of £170 per annum, and by the middle of May he was back after three weeks in Switzerland.

Seligman was now spoiling to get going. He had looked at several possible sites around London but in the end had picked on one at Point Pleasant in Wandsworth, part of an old disused maltings (Illustration 3). This was leased at a rent of £140 for the first year and £145 for the next two with an option to extend for a further seven years. By mid-June, Seligman was installed there.

A name had to be given to the company. Seligman proposed 'The Aluminium Welding Company', but finally 'The Aluminium Plant and Vessel Company Limited' was agreed and registered on 31 May 1910.

In the meantime, the Articles of Association were being drawn up and agreed. The Certificate of Incorporation was granted on 10 June. The Aluminium Plant and Vessel Company Limited was in being.

## Chapter 2
# Early Years
# 1910-1914

The Board of the Aluminium Plant and Vessel Company Limited met for the first time on June 20th 1910 at Dr Moritz' home.

Its first duty was to receive the Certificate of Incorporation of the company dated ten days earlier which, in turn, was based on the Memorandum of Association under the Companies (Consolidated) Act of 1908. These had only five clauses: the name, England as the situation of the registered office, limited liability of members, authorised capital and objects. The chief business of the company was firstly to acquire patents and licences for the welding and working of aluminium and to exploit them; secondly to carry on a manufacturing and contracting business as mechanical, electrical or water supply engineers, metallurgists, brass founders and to 'deal in machinery, implements and hardware of all kinds'.

The authorised capital of the company was £5,000 (equivalent to about £100,000 today) divided into 5,000 shares of £1 each.

The Board then elected Dr Moritz, Chairman, Dr Seligman, Managing Director, H. F. Fuller, a Director, and A. Winslo, Company Secretary. They also appointed J. Gallon as Works Manager and A. F. Hussey as Chemist. The employees totalled eight in all. The lease for the Point Pleasant factory and office was ratified and various financial matters involved in setting up the company were settled.

The initial issue of shares was decided to be 2,000 of which one each was allotted fully paid to Moritz and Fuller while Seligman took the rest. The amount to be paid immediately was 7s 6d. This

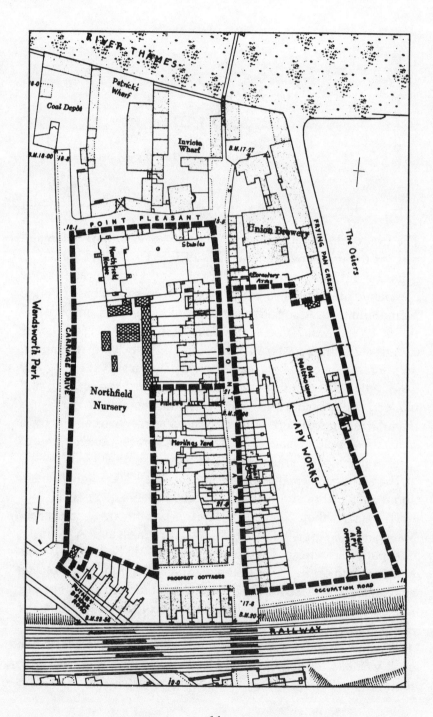

RIVER THAMES

Patrick's Wharf

Coal Depôt

Invicta Wharf

B.M.17·27

Union Brewery

FRYING PAN CREEK

The Osiers

POINT PLEASANT

Northfield House

Stables

Brewery Arms

Wandsworth Park

CARRIAGE DRIVE

Northfield Nursery

Old Malthouse

POINT

APV WORKS

FISHERS ALLEY

B.M.

Marlings Yard

ORIGINAL APV OFFICES

PROSPECT COTTAGES

OCCUPATION ROAD

PUTNEY BRIDGE ROAD

B.M.23·54

B.M.20·27

RAILWAY

provided a sum of about £750 as working capital which did little more than meet the costs of establishing the company.

The site of the factory (Fig. 1) was in part of a disused maltings just north of the railway line from Clapham Junction to Putney, between it and the Thames, in a rather decrepit turning off the Putney Bridge Road, curiously named Point Pleasant and lying at no great distance from the pretty little Wandsworth Park on the west and the huge Wandsworth gas works on the east. A higgledy-piggledy mass of small workshops and cottages were built around, and in some cases over, an inlet called Frying Pan Creek that Nelson was said to have used on his visits to Lady Hamilton at Merton Place, a few miles away. These rather sleazy surroundings were to be the home of APV for over forty years.

The only job on the books was the order for the Gravesend brewery (Illustration 4) but this was immediately doubled by Russell's ordering a second one before the first had even been started. Both Seligman and Moritz were active in seeking business with a good deal of success but, by August, Seligman was envisaging being short of work. By November, this had become acute although further orders had done something to alleviate matters.

The accounts for 1910 show that the sales amounted to about £550 against expenses of £2,880. The discrepancy had been met by calling up the rest of the subscription due on Seligman's shares but there was also the capital expenditure on plant, tools, office and laboratory equipment, experimental work and so on, amounting to about £1,500. It is not recorded how this was met but another 500 shares were allotted to Seligman before the end of the year and a further 500 early in 1911 specifically 'to provide further funds'.

In view of the fact that there was something over £100-worth of stock and £1, 875 of work in progress, the company was well in the red at the end of 1910 as, indeed, might have been expected. At the

Fig. 1. *(opposite)* Sketch map of the Point Pleasant area c. 1910. The dotted line shows the eventual extent of the APV property in 1955.

start it had been thought that brewery business in fermenting and conditioning vessels would be sufficient to keep the company going. It now looked as though this were not going to be so. Seligman looked to other products for the brewery – casks, yeast waggons and vats – and had some success. But there were the inevitable teething troubles with the new plant to be overcome as well as the wary conservatism of brewers, political difficulties that inhibited capital expenditure in breweries and the attempts of not-too-scrupulous established competitors to suggest that they could manufacture just as effectively in aluminium as this new upstart company.

It is difficult to realise how precarious Seligman's position was. We are nowadays so accustomed to plant made in corrosion-resistant sheet materials that it is necessary to try and envisage the situation as it faced him and Moritz.

At that time almost all fermenting vessels were made of copper but, at the end of 1908, a prominent brewery consultant, A. Chaston Chapman, had shown that small quantities of copper in solution seriously affected the reproductive power of yeast. Moritz' experiments using the sample vessels from Zürich, backed by the experience, still very short, with the lined fermenter at Fuller, Smith and Turner, suggested that aluminium would not have this effect. But aluminium vessels were not much different in price from copper ones though they were easier to clean and maintain. Conditioning vessels, on the other hand, were almost always made of glass-enamelled steel. These were relatively cheap but heavy, fragile and hard to maintain. Aluminium offered great advantages but there were still doubts as to whether beer would mature properly in aluminium tanks.

On the other hand, Seligman had a unique patented process for fabricating a new material of valuable properties, particularly its lightness and corrosion resistance. Moreover, he and his workforce not only knew how to weld aluminium but had the know-how, at that time a jealously guarded secret, of hammering and annealing the welds to give the proper metallurgical structure without which the welds were relatively brittle. This gave the company a strong position technically as well as legally.

Even more important was Seligman's own character and convictions. One of the first things he did at Wandsworth was to set up a laboratory and chemist to carry out experimental investigations as well as control. He was then, as always, convinced that a technical business could only be carried on effectively if it were backed by proper scientific staff and facilities.

Seligman was, however, having difficulties in one area where, perhaps, he least expected it. The agreement with AAS had been signed and ratified by the end of July 1910 but almost immediately there were difficulties. If the value of the patents was to be maintained, then the Swiss had to take action against anyone infringing them as they had undertaken to do under the agreement. This, however, they seemed very loath to do until they were threatened by loss of royalties unless they complied. During this first critical year and, indeed, thereafter, Seligman and Moritz had to spend a quite inordinate proportion of their time in wrangles that should never have arisen. Eventually, early in 1911, the Swiss company successfully applied for an injunction restraining a competitor from infringing their patents. This, however, did not finally settle the matter and disputes of one kind or another over infringements and other matters affecting the agreement continued.

Towards the end of 1910, Seligman began to feel that more experimental work was needed than he or Moritz could effectively carry out in their laboratories. When he was not supervising the design and fabrication work at Wandsworth, he was chasing up and down the country for orders, trouble-shooting or dealing with administrative matters and had no time to direct research. It was therefore decided to ask Chaston Chapman, who had done the work on the deleterious effect of copper on brewers' yeast, to undertake a similar investigation on the effect of aluminium.

Towards the end of 1911, Chapman published an authoritative paper in which he referred to the satisfactory state of, and results obtained with, the lined fermenter at Chiswick and described experiments, similar to those he had made earlier with copper, that led him to conclude that aluminium was chemically well suited for brewery plant.

At the beginning of 1911 P. N. ('Patsy') Norman was appointed Works Manager, the first of a series of able assistants who left their mark on the company over many years of service.

The names of the first coppersmiths are not known for certain. They certainly included Harlock who, with his son, had been involved with the Swiss welder Fässler in fabricating the Chiswick vessel. Harlock senior was the first APV coppersmith and his son became carpenter. E. W. ('Ted') Whitlock, later to become Works Manager and first employee Director, joined a few weeks later.

In spite of the anxieties, 1911 went much as might have been expected. The total sales were slightly over £7,000 and the expenses some £500 greater; the work in progress and so the forward work load had been very substantially reduced. Overall the operation for the year showed a loss of some £1,200. This was not really unsatisfactory and the shop was kept pretty full throughout the year.

While most of the substantial work was for breweries and there was a host of small jobs for all sorts of firms, by far the largest single contract, over £2,300 in all, was for a company, Solutal Ltd, laid through H. F. Fuller. This must have been a malt extract plant at Chiswick about which there had been some discussion in the previous year.

The largest single items, amounting together to more than half the contract price, were for 'designing and providing plant' and 'erection'. It was therefore very much a contracting job although it is not clear how much was bought out. Certainly the evaporator was from J. A. Reavell's Kestner Evaporator and Engineering

Company – many years later to become a member of the APV group.

Solutal must have been a crucial job for the young company. It provided badly needed work and finance at the end of 1910 and beginning of 1911, and it must have supported a larger and more sophisticated engineering staff than perhaps might have been expected.

Most of the brewery work was concerned with fermenters and yeast vessels and many of the great names in the brewery world appear in the sales for 1911. Sales were, however, badly affected by unexpected corrosion in the conditioning tanks at Chiswick and Gravesend. At one time it looked as though the tanks at Russell's would be thrown out. The news spread through the industry like wildfire, as such news will, and lost nothing in the telling. The cause was never finally proved although, with hindsight, we can presume that it was associated with the use of estuarine water for cleaning. In the end, after the cleaning methods and general housekeeping had been improved, the corrosion at both breweries came to a halt. But much damage had been done. Neither Seligman nor Moritz wished themselves or the company to be associated with a faulty product, so sales were halted from February to October. In the meantime, prospective brewery customers were demanding guarantees of the life of aluminium plant, competitors were blackguarding aluminium and, at one time, even Moritz lost his nerve and suggested glass enamelling the inside of the tanks at Gravesend.

By October, things were looking up. Nevertheless, it was becoming clear that the brewery business alone would be insufficient to support the company and at the Board meeting on 30 May 1911, this was accepted and it was agreed to pursue business in the chemical industries.

This was done and among the companies laying orders during 1911 are several of significance. One of the first was for Keiller's jam factory for lining steam-jacketed pans for making marmalade. Through Keiller's, Seligman came in contact with Loders and

Nucoline, a Silvertown firm handling edible oils from whom he got his first order for an oil deodoriser. This was a quite remarkable construction under the circumstances. It consisted of an almost flat pan some 6 ft in diameter surmounted by a short belt and a hemispherical dome. As this had to work under high vacuum and at comparatively high temperature, there was virtually no mechanical data on which to base a design nor was there anyone at Wandsworth capable of designing such a vessel if there had been. Norman thought that 10 gauge would be thick enough, Seligman that it would be on the thin side. To settle the matter they had recourse to experiment. A full-sized 10 gauge conditioning vessel was put under vacuum and, to Norman's horror, collapsed.

On this rather haphazard basis, the vessel was designed and built (Illustration 5). This started what was to be an important line for the company in its early years. Aluminium causes no discoloration of the oils treated in it nor does it catalyse rancidity as does copper; thus it enabled considerable improvements in the use and treatment of edible oils, particularly for margarine production, to be made.

Soon after, Seligman met an old college friend who was employed by Otto Monsted, the great margarine firm of Southall. From them came a long string of orders for deodorisers, waggons, churns, transport and storage tanks, the first of which were supplied that year.

All these companies and some others were in the food rather than chemical industries. Nevertheless, a number of important truly chemical companies appear in the list of sales for this year, Burroughs, Wellcome; Boake, Roberts; and the Royal Gunpowder Factory among them. The company had shown its ability to involve itself successfully in other industries than brewing although, curiously enough in view of its subsequent history, not with milk and dairying. It had also demonstrated its ability to design and put down complete plants and did not need to confine itself to the manufacture of simple tanks and linings.

The big extension of sales contacts demanded increase in staff and in the middle of 1911 two representatives were appointed. Questions of foreign representation, particularly in Australia, also came up. J. W. Wilson, who was destined to play a large part in the development of the company over the next thirty years or so and at that time associated with the *Brewery Trades Review*, was asked to advise on the merits of the various firms and people who had applied for the Australian agency. This involved the whole question of the company's rights to the 'colonial' patents of AAS, Zürich, and, by extension, Seligman's position under his agency agreement with the Swiss company. However, it could not be pursued because during the whole of 1912 there was another squabble with the Swiss about their taking action over infringement, culminating again in a legal threat to withhold royalties and the Swiss climbing down.

The higher level of manufacturing and sales activity demanded increases in working capital. By the end of 1911, the whole authorised capital of £5,000 had been issued and paid for. All of the extra shares were taken up by Richard Seligman except one that was allotted to his younger brother, Gerald, who had been elected to the Board in May.

This issue of shares proved insufficient and, in November, Richard Seligman made a loan to the company of a further £1,000, a loan that was increased in 1912 and was £8,265 by the end of 1913. By then his investment in the company was £11,595, some of his shares having been transferred to Gerald. This is a measure of his entrepreneurial capacity; he had been prepared to invest a sum equivalent to about £230,000 at today's values without return. Some of it was provided indirectly by Seligman Brothers, though how much at this stage is not recorded.

In the middle of 1912, J. W. Wilson was elected a Director and, although he had no executive responsibilities, his influence became apparent almost at once. The number of Board meetings increased and business at them became more succinct.

In October an important Board meeting was held attended by all the Directors and also Richard's elder brother, Charles (later Sir Charles), of Seligman Brothers, at which 'the question of continuing the business was carefully considered'. Nothing is known as to what was said or what guarantees, if any, were given. However, as the Board minute laconically states, 'it was agreed to continue'.

Nevertheless, the year 1912, in spite of the doubts and anxieties, was a year of progress and consolidation. The sales rose to just about £10,000 and, as there was not a corresponding increase in expenses, the overall result was practically a break-even. It seems, especially in view of the discussion about continuing the business, that this was something of a pleasant surprise to the Board. There was no large installation like Fuller's Solutal. Instead there was a large number and wide variety of smaller jobs. Breweries still accounted for the largest proportion of turnover but the edible oil industry was becoming important; Loders and Nucoline were the largest customers and Otto Monsted was beginning to lay important orders.

An interesting development of the oil business, the varnish industry, appears this year for the first time. In those days, varnish was widely used to protect wood. It was based almost entirely on linseed oil which was 'boiled' by heating it in a pot over an open fire or by burners using gas or oil. Aluminium, with its high thermal conductivity and ability not to discolour the oil as iron or copper were likely to do, proved an ideal material of construction. One of the centres of the industry was at Mitcham, only a mile or two down the road from Wandsworth, so it was a natural development. For the next thirty years, the varnish industry was to provide a limited but significant proportion of the company's business until linseed oil was displaced by synthetic polymers and aluminium by stainless steel after the Second World War.

The sales in 1912 were divided into 44% brewery, 16% chemical, 16% oils and fats, 7% varnish and 17% sundries, including food.

By 1912, the company consisted of nine staff and twenty to

twenty-five works employees (Illustration 6). The sales force badly needed strengthening and in August Patsy Norman was transferred from the works at a remuneration of 5% commission, with a minimum salary of £200 p.a. and expenses of 10s (50p) per day (5s in London), not including Saturdays, plus rail fares. He was to cover Scotland as well, and perhaps Ireland too, if milk business were to be developed.

The first steps were also taken towards establishing overseas agencies. Australia was the first objective. It was decided to give the agency to F. A. Henriques Ltd and an agreement was signed. Naturally enough the question of repairs to vessels arose and AAS in Zürich were asked to grant Henriques the right to use the process under their Australian patent. They replied that they had granted exclusive rights to another firm several months before. This was thought to violate the agreement and there followed yet another altercation between the two companies. Eventually a Heads of Terms Compromise was signed but not until October 1914. In the meantime, Henriques seems to have gone on quietly getting business in Australia and New Zealand for Wandsworth until his agreement expired at the end of 1915.

The demands for space became greater as the business grew. At the Board meeting where the future of the company was debated it had been decided to stay in the premises for three years at least but to provide the necessary extensions by renting a vacant building in the yard and to erect a further temporary building later if it were needed. By the end of 1913 the premises had been acquired and the work of conversion put in hand. Later, in 1913, further leases were signed and Point Pleasant became the permanent home of the company.

During 1912, Moritz, though continuing as Chairman, started to play a less prominent role in the company. Mostly he was involved with the AAS agreement and the disputes arising from it as well as brewery contacts, but much less with test work and day-to-day affairs. Nevertheless he must have been of great value to the company. Consultants were much more powerful in breweries then than they could be now. There was a large number of small brewery companies, hardly any of them with the resources to maintain an adequate technical staff. The consultant provided the technical competence that was lacking and his opinion was unlikely to be ignored. The advice Moritz gave to Seligman on where to seek orders, and to brewers on the advantages of aluminium, must have been invaluable.

From two points of view, 1913 was a turning point in the life of the company. In the first place, it was the first year in which a profit was made. The turnover of about £17,800 gave a profit on the year of some £1,725 that wiped out the deficit of the previous three years' operations and left a positive balance of about £300. A dividend of 5¾% was paid and a start made in writing off the costs of setting up the company.

Sales were for the most part similar to the previous year but there were several major contracts for vegetable oils. As a result the proportion of turnover for oils and fats increased substantially. The figures were: brewery 38%, chemical 12%, oils and fats 34%, varnish 7% and sundries 9%.

In the second place, Seligman obtained the rights to a process, the Scott yeast plant, based on vessels manufactured at Wandsworth and protected by patent. It was to prove a money-spinner and set the stage for a number of such process developments that have played a major part in establishing the firm's prosperity.

The process is basically a simple one. The yeast left after beer has been run off from a fermenting vessel contains a high proportion of beer. Before Scott's process was introduced the mixture was held for some time to allow gas to escape and then pumped through a filter thus removing the yeast and recovering the beer as filtrate. The process took a considerable time to carry out and the high turbulence in the pump ruptured some of the yeast cells so causing off-flavours in the beer, while deterioration and infection resulted from the need to hold and the generally poor control. Walter Scott, Chief Brewer of Ansells' Brewery, Birmingham, had the idea of feeding the mixture of yeast and beer to a pressure vessel, subjecting it to vacuum to remove entrained gas and then forcing the mixture under air pressure through a filter press where the yeast was removed and the beer recovered without pumping or having to allow time for gas to disengage under normal pressure. In this way beer was recovered without delay, there was the minimum risk of infection and deterioration, no 'yeast bite' flavour appeared in the beer and the yeast was collected and could be stored in the press under the most favourable conditions; economies were made in labour and, most important of all, the beer was recovered in full.

It was this last that made the process so attractive. In Britain, duty is paid on the volume and density of the wort before fermentation. Any extra yield of beer over the normal is therefore equivalent to a recovery duty free. Outside Britain, however, duty is normally paid on the finished beer so that this advantage does not arise to the same extent. This, and the difference in handling bottom fermentation lager yeasts, account for the fact that the process has been relatively little used outside these Islands. Here, however, it became virtually standard practice and it is not too much to say that it revolutionised yeast handling in breweries especially in the more sophisticated forms in which it was later developed.

It was in early 1913 that Scott approached Seligman to manufacture plant for him. Seligman at once saw the possibilities of the process and persuaded Scott that the company should offer the process to other brewers and collect a royalty for him. Ansells' agreed, Moritz was enthusiastic, the process was patented and aroused great interest at the Brewers' show. After a good deal of prevarication, an agreement was signed in September 1914. The process became one of the most important activities of the company for many years to come.

It was no matter of chance that Seligman latched on to this

process. He, and Moritz too, were always on the lookout for new products. Road tankers for beer were developed. Following on this Seligman proposed a scheme for transporting pasteurised beer and, although Moritz poured cold water on it, he in turn proposed the use of aluminium cellar tanks in public houses containing filtered and pasteurised beer under $CO_2$ pressure to replace casks. Both schemes came to nought but they were imaginative and before their time. Now they are commonplace.

The results for 1914 were again better. Sales were nearly £25,400 and profit, after write-offs and deducting royalties, was £1,950. Practically the whole profit was paid out to the shareholders in a dividend of 37½% and nothing was put to reserve.

The sort of work undertaken was much as in the year before. This was to change radically but in 1914, during which hostilities broke out on 4 August, the effect of the war seems to have been negligible.

The level of remuneration at this time was not exactly princely. There is no exact record of wage rates but they must have been under a shilling (5p) an hour. The oncost rate was calculated on the basis of 88,000 productive hours per annum for 1913, equivalent to some thirty men working fifty-six hours a week, twelve of whom were coppersmiths. It was fixed at 10½d per hour and was increased to 1s per hour for 1914.

The hours worked were certainly very long. Early in 1914 the rule relating to pay for men working sixty-eight and a quarter hours per week on outside jobs was amended to cover fifty-six hours per week. These seem to have been the standard hours of work.

A Social and Sports Club must have been founded quite early on in the history of the company for by the end of 1912 the Board was agreeing to contribute up to £25 towards the club's expenses depending on the members' subscriptions.

In charge of the works was J. French as Foreman from mid-1912 and E. Stanley as Works Manager. He had been appointed towards the end of 1914 to succeed, at long last, Patsy Norman. At the end of 1913 an apprenticeship agreement (was it the first?) was sealed with S. W. ('Bill') Paine, later to become Brewery Sales Manager. His father was already employed as a coppersmith. Bill, in later years, used to amuse his friends with a graphic description of how father and son started on foot from the East End at six in the morning and proceeded to Wandsworth, partly on foot and partly by tram, calling in frequently at the pubs, many of which were open at that hour, to arrive thoroughly well oiled after a journey lasting the best part of a couple of hours. The journey home was much the same but more expansive. How they got any sleep baffles imagination.

But the most important addition to the staff at this time was Percy Williams. Seligman had met him during his brief employment at British Uralite in 1903. Earlier he had worked at University College as assistant to Sir William Ramsay and was involved in the work that led to the discovery of argon. From Higham he went to Borneo, where he stayed happily until 1911 when he returned to England finally to join Seligman in Wandsworth as chemist, a post he retained to the day of his death in 1942.

He was an extraordinary man, very shy, completely unambitious, lovable and wholly dedicated to his work. He had practically no other interests and no social life.

He was a brilliant experimental chemist with an encyclopaedic knowledge and a flair for the simple, crucial experiment that would finally resolve a problem. He scorned complex apparatus and always made his own. He was indeed the archetype of the chemist of the old school. He was always content to follow a lead and so was the perfect foil to Seligman. Together they made a brilliant team and much first-class work, both published and unpublished, was to stem from this partnership.

So, by the end of 1914, the stage was set. The company had proved its viability and had started on the course of technical development and expansion that was to be its hallmark. Seligman, with his remarkable flair for picking the right, if unlikely looking man, was already gathering an excellent team about him. All seemed set for further relatively unruffled progress when the First World War intervened.

## Chapter 3
# The First World War
# 1914–1918

The company entered the war years having established itself as an effective specialist fabricating firm supplying welded vessels mainly to the brewery and vegetable oil trades. It now had a total of sixty employees and had shown that it could operate profitably. Although it did not possess a particularly impressive factory nor have much in the way of sophisticated tools, it could look forward to steady expansion in its chosen fields.

The war was to alter all that. To start with this was not obviously apparent. The first few weeks went by in a state of public euphoria. It was only when the devastating German advance had been halted before Paris and the struggle had settled down to the dreadful ineffectiveness of trench warfare with its occasional bouts of appalling slaughter, that the full meaning of modern warfare dawned on the country.

At Wandsworth, it was first felt when the use of aluminium for breweries was prohibited. It was all needed for essential munitions plant. The company had to look elsewhere for work. At first it appeared a daunting prospect but this proved to be a pessimistic view. The company was the only one in the country able to produce welded equipment in aluminium needed for the war effort. As a result, absolutely new fields of work were opened up.

This was by no means unwelcome to Seligman. Already early in 1914 he had voiced his disappointment with the brewery business in a letter to Moritz and even suggested dropping it altogether. In fact during the war the turnover of the company increased rapidly and,

29

with it, the demands on the Managing Director's energies. In the latter part of the war, both Gerald Seligman and Wilson enlisted, so that the whole management devolved on Richard Seligman and Moritz. The burden was a heavy and frustrating one. The end of the war in November 1918 settled it all but only just in time to stop Seligman having a serious breakdown.

The main war work undertaken by the company fell into two main categories, explosives and aircraft. The company was heavily engaged in equipping the new large explosive factories, including storage tanks and other plant used in the production and handling of nitric acid and explosives derived from it. The excellent resistance of aluminium to corrosion by strong nitric acid and, particularly, its non-sparking characteristics made it an essential material of construction for such applications.

Up to the outbreak of war the country was dependent very largely on Germany for the supply of chemicals. In consequence there was an almost total lack of plants to produce the basic synthetic materials for chemical and particularly explosive production. One of these was acetone, an essential ingredient in the production of cordite, the standard propellant for heavy gun shells. The usual method of production was cumbersome and expensive but, in 1912, Dr Chaim Weizmann, afterwards President of Israel, had discovered that a bacterium could ferment sugars and starches to acetone and butyl alcohol, the latter a useful solvent for paints and aircraft dopes. The process had been tried out on a commercial scale in 1913–14 and was clearly the best way to provide for rapid expansion. Seligman worked closely with Weizmann whom he had known for some time as a Zionist. The plant required was all designed at Wandsworth and the fermenting vessels were built there. Later on, manufacture of acetone by the Weizmann process was transferred to Canada and the United States to be nearer the source of raw materials. The plant was manufactured locally and Wandsworth was denied any part in the enormous development of the process that followed.

During the early part of the war the company made over a building it had recently acquired on the Wandsworth site to Weizmann to convert to a laboratory where he and a team of bacteriologists and chemists carried on the control and development work essential to the process. This was kept highly secret and, naturally enough, imagination among the company's workforce ran riot. The grapevine, unreliable as ever, reported that work was proceeding on poison gas and TNT, a view that was only reinforced when one day at dinner time there was a huge explosion followed by a fire in which a woman scientist died.

That finished the Weizmann laboratory and it was then converted to a light coppersmith shop to carry on the second main wartime activity of the company, the manufacture of aluminium petrol tanks, first for coastal defence airships and, later, for aeroplanes.

The company's entry into this field was somewhat casual. It was reported that a Zeppelin airship had been hit over Essex and that an aluminium tank shot out of it had been found. Seligman secured permission to see it. The man who showed it to him complained that no such tank was made in Britain. Seligman offered to make them at once and a few days later the first airship tanks in aluminium produced in this country were made.

From that day until the end of the war, the new light shop was fully engaged in the production of petrol and similar tanks (Illustration 7). It was there that women welders, trained by the company's coppersmiths, were first employed.

In spite of all the difficulties, the brewery work still continued sporadically, mainly Scott yeast plants for which a case could be made as saving appreciable quantities of raw materials.

This period also saw the start of some fundamental work on the corrosion of aluminium carried out by Percy Williams under Seligman's direction. The work was no doubt stimulated by the new uses for the metal in explosive and chemical factories. Much of it was published in a series of classic papers but it represents only a fraction of Williams' investigations which, in one way or another, covered the whole range of the company's activities.

During the war years, the turnover increased substantially from £38,750 in 1915 to £107,000 in 1918. The corresponding profits before tax were £5,276 and £11,000.

But the company was not allowed to retain a major part of its profits. In order to combat war profiteering, the Government introduced an excess profits duty. This hit a growing company like the APV Company particularly hard and they lost at a stroke half, and in some years much more, of their profits.

New working capital was needed to finance the expansion of the business. Some of this was provided by loans. Richard Seligman increased his lending to the company by some £4,000. Most of this seems to have come indirectly from Seligman Brothers.

In June 1915 the authorised share capital was increased from £5,000 to £15,000 and 5,000 shares were distributed among Moritz, Richard and Gerald Seligman.

In spite of cash restrictions, the finances were put on a more satisfactory footing. The expenses incurred in setting up the company were almost written off. £4,000 was put to reserve; directors' fees were agreed and a salary paid to the Managing Director for the first time in 1916. Modest dividends of 15% for 1915 and 1916 were paid, but none for 1917 and only 5% for 1918.

In spite of the war, there were still some troubles with AAS, Zürich. In the main these arose once again over infringement and the difficulty of getting AAS to take action to maintain the patents. Early in 1915, several cases were brought to Zürich's notice and eventually they agreed to leave it to the company to take action on their behalf. Things dragged on, however, until some welded aluminium cans bearing the name of the London Aluminium Company, Birmingham, were sent to Wandsworth for repair. This was conclusive evidence of infringement, but it took five years or so before the case was finally settled.

During these years the workforce and staff were about doubled and many familiar APV names appear in the records for the first time. Winlo resigned at the beginning of 1918 and was replaced as Acting Secretary by T. C. Wallis, who was to hold this and similar posts for many years to come. In the works, Jack French had his agreement as Works Foreman renewed for two years and he was even granted a fortnight's holiday.

Pay in those days was very low even allowing for change in the value of money. Stanley, as Works Manager, was paid £200 per annum while the total remuneration for the company's staff in 1915 only amounted to £1,890 per annum.

The company suffered very few direct effects of the war. The men were all in reserved occupations and except for members of the Board were little affected by the war outside their jobs. In the absence of any serious bomb attacks life seems to have gone on much as before for most of the employees, and food rationing was much less effective than in the Second World War.

The big increase in production required an extension of premises (Illustration 8). The original buildings consisted of the old maltings and a tiny office building. This housed the administrative and general offices with a miniscule laboratory and a drawing office in the basement. The old maltings was divided in half by a wall down the middle and accommodated stores, maintenance engineer and power plant as well as the coppersmith shop. The plant was pretty rudimentary. Besides the welding equipment, there was a mechanical hammer-press, plate rolls, one or two lathes, a milling machine and a mechanical drill. In an open-fronted shed outside there was a blacksmiths' shop where back flanges and mild steel supporting frames were made. The power supply for the main shop came from a highly temperamental old gas engine driving the various machines through an overhead shaft and belting.

The first extension of premises was the acquisition of two buildings close by, one of which was made over to Weizmann as a laboratory and then eventually became the light coppersmith shop. The second became the blacksmiths' shop.

By early 1915 the Board had decided to embark on the construction of a new coppersmiths' shop. This meant acquiring land and some existing buildings from Leather, the owner of the site. The freehold was acquired in June, and work started. It was finished together with some extension to the offices by the end of the year.

As early as 1914 a diminutive foundry was in operation but the transfer of coppersmithing work to the new 'heavy' shop provided space for a new and rather better equipped foundry in the decrepit old maltings and an extension alongside it.

Later on, a new building was erected alongside the office. This became the drawing office thus releasing the draughtsmen from their bench in the cellar.

Among the lads serving their seven years' apprenticeship at this time was Percy Talman. His father, Henry, was storekeeper at Point Pleasant when he entered his indentures in 1913. He has recorded a lively account of life in the Wandsworth shops at the time, as seen by an apprentice.

Boys left school at fourteen in those days and so had far less schooling than the young men entering industry nowadays. Life was a lot rougher too. The apprentice, like all journeymen, was expected to provide his own tools and Talman set out on his first day with a set given him by various members of his family.

When he got to work at 6.45 a.m. by tram, he was given instructions by the Foreman, Jack French, a bowler-hatted figure of the old school. They included every sort of menial job as well as helping the men and learning his trade until he started for home at 6.00 p.m. (12.30 p.m. on Saturdays). It was a 60-hour week with two hours overtime a night in wartime.

Talman was put under Ted Whitlock as chargehand whom he came to like and respect but before he could start he had to undergo a sadistic initiation ceremony. Such horseplay was common. When he finished his time there was another ceremony of the same kind to celebrate his becoming a qualified craftsman.

Not all the pranks were so rough. Once in a while the men used to

1. Richard Seligman, founder of The A.P.V. Company Ltd.;
Managing Director 1910 to 1931; Chairman 1931 to 1958.

2. First welded aluminium-lined fermenter at Fuller, Smith and Turner's Chiswick brewery (19

3. APV's first workshop. The o maltings at Point Pleasant.

*Facing page:*

4. (Above) APV's first job: a weld aluminium beer conditioning ves for Russell's Gravesend brewery (1910).

5. (Below) The first edible oil vac deodoriser in aluminium for Lode and Nucoline being carted up P Pleasant (1911).

6. On the company's first annual outing at Southend (1912). In the back row in a cap is Richard Seligman with Jack French, Works Foreman, in a stylish trilby and Patsy Norman, Works Manager, in a boater on either side of him. The young man second from left in the front row is Bill Paine, first draughtsman and apprentice.

7. APV coppersmiths among welded aluminium airship fuel tanks (1917). The heavily moustached figure in the middle row is 'old' Fred Harlock, the company's first coppersmith.

decide that they would like an outing on the river, not surprisingly considering the hours they worked. The final decision was made by getting the youngest apprentice to throw a brick into the air. If it came down, they took the afternoon off. On one occasion, the apprentice, in an excess of zeal, threw the brick so high that it came down on the roof and stuck in the gutter. The men were so abashed that they went back to work (or so Whitlock used to relate).

The apprentices had a pretty hard existence and pay was minimal. Talman's indentures show that he started at 7s (35p) per week rising to 21s (£1.05) per week in his last year.

The training that the apprentices were given was broad. As well as their specialised training, three months were spent in the drawing office and another two in the foundry. Three evenings a week were spent compulsorily at the Battersea Polytechnic.

The apprentices also mixed the patent flux and formed the so-called welding sticks used in the gas welding process. In this they were instructed personally by either Richard or Gerald Seligman. In these early days, Richard took an active part in the day-to-day operation of the works and was in close personal touch with his workpeople. Indeed, until literally the last day of his life, he made a daily solitary tour of the works.

During these war years the company had certainly proved itself. It had become a unique contributor to the war effort; it and its staff had acquired a national reputation and it had demonstrated its ability to seize opportunities of expansion to meet the needs of the country. In doing so, it had acquired a certain stability.

And then the war came to an end with the armistice of 11 November 1918 almost as suddenly as it had started. With it all the war work practically ceased and the company was faced with finding a proper role for itself in the years that lay ahead.

## Chapter 4
# Crisis and Recovery
## 1919–1923

At the beginning of 1919, two problems faced the company, one immediate and obvious, the other deeper but more serious. They were to govern the development of the Aluminium Plant and Vessel Company over the next five years and result in a pattern for its business that has dominated it ever since.

It had been clear for some time that the financial and organisational structure was far from satisfactory. On the one hand, too much reliance was being put on borrowing as a source of working capital. At the same time, altogether too much of the day-to-day management had devolved on Richard Seligman so that by the end of the war he was near to breakdown even though Moritz, under pressure, had undertaken to look after the financial and secretarial side and, for a short time, did so.

Tackling these difficulties thus became the Board's first priority. But behind lay the more important problem of what sort of business was going to be able to provide the work that the factory and workforce at Wandsworth, now much larger than they had been at the start of the war, would require if the company was to remain profitable.

Moritz and Seligman pinned their faith at first on the chemical industry. They quite rightly foresaw that the country would not again permit itself to be so totally dependent on imported chemicals as it had been before the war. This would need huge extensions of chemical plant of all sorts. Where they erred was in over-estimating the part that the company would be able to play in this. In a sense, success in the wartime chemical industries had come too easily, involving, as it did, products and processes for which aluminium was peculiarly well suited.

They were reinforced in their view by the low level to which the brewing industry had been brought by the restrictions imposed during the war.

Then came a big increase in beer duty. This could have been expected to have a disastrous effect on the company's business. Actually, it proved a blessing in disguise for it greatly increased the savings that could be achieved by installation of a Scott yeast plant and few sizeable breweries could afford to be without one. Production, held back for about five years, burgeoned and by the end of 1923, 140 plants had been sold. Nevertheless, it became obvious that the basis for the business as a whole was too narrow and would have to be broadened.

The first priorities, however, remained the financial and administrative ones. In March 1919, it was decided to increase the authorised capital from £15,000 to £35,000. The £4,000 put to reserve was then distributed in the form of new shares to the existing shareholders. A further 1,940 shares were issued in proportion to Richard and Gerald Seligman, and Moritz.

But all of this was to prove quite insufficient. In February 1919 the Board had made what turned out to be a disastrous appointment. So much so that Seligman afterwards described the years immediately following the war as the blackest that the company had had. Although the switch to civilian work was taking place relatively easily, the management were disorganised and tired out. It seemed obvious that something radical must be done, so they decided to appoint a General Manager to reorganise the company and its administration. He called himself a professional organiser, trained in the Taylor system, at that time thought to be the panacea for all industrial ills, now quite forgotten.

The Board at first gave him full scope. Soon, however, they began to feel, as Seligman afterwards put it, 'organised and reorganised and ultimately so disorganised' that failure looked imminent.

The General Manager was dismissed in March 1920 but the results of bad management lived on after him. During that year the direct charges, wages and materials, and the office overheads increased by over a half. Although the turnover for 1919 was about £93,000 the profit fell to less than £2,200 as compared with £11,000 on a similar turnover in 1918. The next year was even worse. The profit fell to a negligible £1,607 on a turnover of £131,000.

The strain on liquidity was severe. The directors either loaned money or gave guarantees on loans from other sources. The dividend of 5% voted in respect of 1919 was left unpaid; and none was paid for 1920. In October 1919, the Board decided on a scheme of further building and resolved on financing this by issuing new shares and raising a mortgage. They can hardly have realised at that juncture how weak their position was. In November Seligman stated to the Board that the company's operations would not be very profitable in the near future. As a result the issue of shares was reduced in December to 16,000. At the same time a loan was sought from the bank. It was refused. The building scheme had to be greatly curtailed and in April 1920 a further 18,000 shares were issued. The total issued capital was now just under £50,000.

The company still had to struggle on with loans to keep it going. The immediate bills for buildings in mid-1920 were met by loans from the directors. A bank overdraft of £5,000 guaranteed personally by the three principal shareholders was negotiated. At this point, Leather chose to foreclose on the mortgage on the works freehold land and property. After some ado it was transferred to the bank.

By the beginning of 1921, however, the corner had been turned and the company was contemplating repayment of some of the loans. Towards the end of 1919, Seligman had determined to try and get Wilson to become a full-time Joint Managing Director to put things to rights. He agreed and started on 1 January 1920. It was a daunting job for he knew exactly how things stood but he was just the man for it. In the years that followed he did magnificent work and within twelve months he had undone most of the mischief that had been done by the Organiser. He was a man who put as his first duty the wellbeing of the company; he saw (or thought he saw) quite clearly how that could be attained; and he was ruthless in achieving it. He did not suffer fools or slackers gladly. He gained the reputation of being a hard man, but he was not really so. Those that did not know him well feared him. But those who knew him best found him scrupulously fair and admired and respected him. He had not Seligman's gift of leadership or ability to command affection, still less his imaginative flair. But he was a first-class commercial man and an excellent foil to Seligman in a team that lasted over twenty years.

Initially he ruled, as he had to, with an iron hand. Anyone doing less than a good day's work went at once. The results were dramatic. The direct wages that had been 28% of turnover in 1911 fell to 16% in 1921 and stayed there. Work in progress was halved. Office salaries and wages were brought down by a third. The only increase was in travellers' salaries. Wilson saw clearly the need to bring down the cost of production but to increase the money spent on selling it.

As a result, although the turnover in 1921 was appreciably lower at £113,000, the profit had risen to over £10,000. The results for 1922 were very similar but for 1923, with a similar turnover, the profit was only a little more than half due to heavy development expenses.

The Articles of Association required that a fair value for the shares be ascertained by the auditors to serve as a basis for any trading in them. These give an interesting evaluation of the state of the company over these years. In June 1920 they were valued at par (£1), in 1921 at 15s (75p); in 1922 at par again and in 1923 at 24s 4d (£1.22). This is a measure of the recovery achieved under Wilson's direction.

During the time of crisis and revision of the company's finances there was a good deal of private discussion between Richard Seligman and Seligman Brothers and it is clear that policy followed their advice. They made several loans but the much better position in 1921 allowed these and most of the shareholders' loans to be paid off. Finally, in 1922, the mortgage from the bank was liquidated.

For 1921 and subsequent years, an interim dividend of 5% subject to tax and a final dividend of 10% free of tax were paid on the much larger share capital.

By 1922, therefore, the operations of the company were at last on a sound footing and the shareholders were getting a return for the risks they had taken. This was the more commendable as it was achieved against some adverse circumstances. The end of the war and the euphoria that followed it resulted in a trade boom that collapsed in the slump of 1921. The normal work of the company seems to have been little affected, certainly it did not prevent the overall improvement in its fortunes, but it did have a disastrous effect on one side of the firm's business.

About the end of the war, it was decided to go into aluminium die-casting. The light coppersmiths' shop was converted into a die-casting foundry. It did some excellent work with the help of an exceptionally clever and industrious die designer but it required specialised management that at that juncture the company could not give it. It lost money but,faced with the cost of winding it up, the Board decided to carry on until conditions for shutting it down were more favourable.

In 1920 a new separate company, The A.P.V. Die-Castings Company Limited, was set up under a specialist in die-casting as Managing Director and with Wilson on the Board. This took over the whole of the company's die-casting business, tools, plant etc. in return for a 50% shareholding.

But this did not eliminate the worries. Already in March 1921 the new company was in debt to the APV Company and so it continued until the 1922 accounts revealed that shares in the die-casting company and their indebtedness to the parent company amounted to £10,000. Wilson reported wholesale cancellation of orders due to the 1921 slump, the position made worse by high metal prices and bad debts. Profits were made in 1923 and 1924 so that by early 1925 it was thought that it might be opportune to dispose of the company. By mid-1926 agreement had been reached to sell off certain of the assets and goodwill at a price that covered all debts and creditors and realised the full value of the shares with a surplus.

So ended the rather melancholy story of the company's first subsidiary. Seligman always regretted going out of the die-casting business just when it was becoming successful, but the decision to do so was sound. It was occupying valuable space and even more valuable management time at a period when the company was just starting to branch out into new and more profitable fields.

In the meantime, considerable changes had taken place in the offices and factory. By mid-1919 a couple of neighbouring cottages had been bought as extra office accommodation and the company was negotiating for extra land that belonged to the Union Brewery Company next door.

At the same time, the lease of Northfields House nearby had been acquired; two years later the freehold of the house and grounds was bought for £2,000. It was close to Point Pleasant and the river, a typical two-storied, mid-Victorian house of some size and elegance. It was an ideal office building for a small company and remained the headquarters of APV until the move to Crawley at the end of 1955.

Towards the end of 1919, it was decided to plan full development of the Point Pleasant site. Eventually a scheme more in keeping with the company's finances was adopted in April 1920. Work was completed at the end of the year and consisted of a new machine shop together with works offices.

Two little cottages acquired in Point Pleasant were converted into a laboratory and a tiny shed outside became the first test house.

There was still trouble with the AAS licence especially over infringement of the patents. The major difficulty centred on the British Aluminium Company. They had never been persuaded of the validity of the Schoop patent and so were perfectly prepared to supply metal to competitors even when it was clear that they were going to use it to infringe Wandsworth's monopoly.

Immediately after the war was over, the Board was urging AAS's lawyers to prosecute an action on their behalf for infringement against the London Aluminium Company. The case was heard in March 1920 and was eventually carried to the House of Lords. It went against London Aluminium. By now it was mid-1922. In the meantime it had been difficult to prevent further minor infringements. It had also been felt for some time that the original agreement needed modification. By the end of 1922 the terms of a new one were agreed, signed and sealed.

In October 1919 H. F. Fuller resigned from the Board. Seligman suggested T. H. Clouston, an engineer, to take his place and he was elected at the beginning of 1920. There were also several changes in Secretary over the period culminating in 1923 in the appointment of H. C. Baigent as Secretary and Accountant, an association that was to last over thirty years.

There were changes, too, in works managership. Early in 1919 the post was taken over by S. J. Ralph and Stanley became Foundry Manager. Ralph was an extraordinary person. A veritable Falstaff of a man, of subtle mind and with a most persuasive tongue, he had great imagination and a remarkable ability to command the affection and loyalty of those who worked for him. He had been trained as a chemist at the Finsbury Technical College under Mendola. He came to Wandsworth from Vickers-Armstrong in Newcastle where he had been working on naval gunsights.

His was a curious appointment as Works Manager, a job for which he was quite unsuited. He was soon replaced by a man supposedly more fully qualified for it and Ralph found his way back to the North of England as a general representative.

Norman had been appointed Chief Engineer but his appointment was terminated at the end of 1920 and he again became a brewery representative under Gerald Seligman who had been made Sales Manager early in 1919. About the same time C. A. Wyatt, later to become the first dairy sales department manager, was appointed as chemical and general salesman.

In the works the activity increased over the period but not greatly in real terms. There were now some eighty productive workers, paid 1s 9d (say 9p) per hour on average and working a fifty-six hour week with no holidays. The total number of employees rose from 140 in 1919 to 175 in 1924, of whom thirty were coppersmiths.

Apart from the Scott yeast plant, other brewery work went well. By the end of 1919 thirty-two breweries had aluminium fermenting vessels. Over the period from 1910 to 1915 the total installed capacity was about 10,000 barrels; by 1923 it was nearly 40,000 barrels, a tenth of the total capacity of the UK breweries.

In addition there were conditioning and bulk transport tanks (horse, rail and lorry), yeast vats and waggons. The storage tanks were of standardised design and could be offered in other industries as, indeed, could many of the other items.

While there was steady work in the food and varnish industries, the edible oil work fell off badly never to recover.

This situation perturbed the Board and particularly Seligman. The works had been substantially enlarged and extra work would be needed to keep them loaded. Where was it to be found?

Seligman was obsessed with two things: that the market for the firm's main bread-winner, the Scott yeast plant, was about to dry up; and that there was a virgin field to cultivate in its stead, the dairy industry. The company should fit itself to enter it.

Moritz and Wilson initially opposed these views. They were convinced that the demand for Scott plants would continue and they were afraid that dealing with anything so innocuous as milk would give offence to the brewers.

Seligman continued to press the dairy business. In November

1920 he produced a report on the possible items that the firm might produce. Interestingly, in view of the developments to come so soon, he ruled out flash pasteurisers and regenerative heaters and coolers. He proposed tanks and vats of various sorts and reckoned that aluminium would be competitive with tinned steel. It offered obvious advantages over the tinned copper and steel or glass-lined equipment used in dairies at that time.

The company took the plunge and started by exhibiting at one dairy show 'in a very small and ineffective way'. The firm's first dairy brochure shows it offering a range of various sorts of open tanks and waggons (loose covers extra); evaporating and steam pans; bulk transport tanks; churns and a host of trays, buckets, scoops, pots and pans.

It was a start but Seligman was convinced that there was much more to do. He became insistent that they ought to inform themselves thoroughly about the industry. He was convinced that big changes would have to take place in the methods of handling milk in this country and that the company should be in a position to benefit by the change when it occurred. Accordingly he got himself familiar with the industry in Britain and Europe. The knowledge he gained there convinced him of two things: first, that it was quite unjustifiable to continue to neglect the quality and, especially, the biological safety of so important a foodstuff as milk and, second, that the UK should not continue to rely on imports of foreign machinery to process it.

His interest now concentrated on the pasteurising process. He found a fairly chaotic state of affairs. There were batch and continuous plants; the pasteurising conditions were variable; the types of plant even more so and of dubious efficiency. At the same time, the introduction of statutory conditions governing pasteurisation in this country was under discussion. A temperature of 145°F (62.8°C) held for thirty minutes was the most favoured combination as it effectively destroyed pathogenic organisms with very little effect on the flavour or cream line.

44

As a first step, the company developed its APV Midget Bulk Pasteuriser, a simple jacketed and stirred covered tank of up to 100 gallons capacity which was heated by steam injected into water in the jacket and cooled by a spray of cold water inside the jacket after draining the hot water from it. Milk was simply brought up to temperature, held there for the requisite time, and cooled. It was the first pasteuriser made in Britain capable of meeting the required pasteurising conditions. It proved popular for many years for small installations.

Seligman was intent, however, on finding out what was happening in the United States and Canada for he believed, quite rightly, that the technique of milk pasteurisation was more advanced there than in Europe. He pressed the Board. At last, after a somewhat stormy Board meeting, Wilson said, 'Why not go to America and see for yourself?' and so, in the autumn of 1921, he did.

Among the many types of apparatus he saw in the United States, two impressed him especially favourably. One was a heater and cooler made by Wisner's of New York, consisting of a bank of double tubes from which the inner tube could be removed for cleaning. Its great advantage was that it could be used for direct regeneration of heat from milk to milk in counter-current and so obtain a much higher regenerative effect than could be attained with other machines. But it was cumbersome and hard to clean as well as requiring a lot of space.

The other was a type of flow holder. At that time, as also for many years after, thought among dairy engineers centred upon the design and construction of plant which would secure the holding of milk at the pasteurising temperature for the requisite time. This particular device, then much favoured in America, consisted of a series of tall narrow tanks through which the milk flowed continuously thereby being held, it was claimed, for the required pasteurising time.

In February 1922, Seligman reported to the Board on his visit. He stated his belief that a large market could be open to the company.

The Board agreed that 'every effort should be made to develop the business' but that this should be done gradually.

Accordingly, based on the information gained in the United States,a flow holder consisting of three horizontal chambers, two or three feet in diameter and up to ten feet long, was put on the market. A brochure was published in which glowing accounts were given of its efficiency. It was shown at the Agricultural Hall in October 1922 and was well received by the industry. A number of potential orders were booked.

In fact the design was abysmally bad. No tests of holding efficiency had been made. The American experience was taken to be sufficient and in any case there was no time if the machine was to be on show that season. When, however, tests were initiated at Wandsworth immediately after the exhibition, they revealed an efficiency far below that anticipated. It was clear that the flow holder as designed could not possibly give the accuracy of holding required for milk pasteurisation.

The position was now very difficult. Customers were already demanding the holder and it could not honourably be supplied. At this point Seligman had a stroke of luck. During the first week of November, W. G. Tarbet, who was working with the company as dairy consultant and adviser, read a description of the Willmann holder which consisted of a set of tanks rotating about, and connected to, a common valve. Each was filled in turn with heated milk which was then held positively for the time required for pasteurisation before discharging. This provided an unequivocal holding time but when coupled to a continuous heater was liable to permit contamination of treated by untreated milk, a fatal drawback.

Tarbet conceived the idea that the inadequacies of the Willmann holder could be overcome if the holding vessel were isolated from any connection with the outside except during filling and emptying. He proposed a nest of half a dozen tanks rotating about a vertical axis, filled at one point in the circuit from above and emptied through a valve at the bottom automatically actuated by an

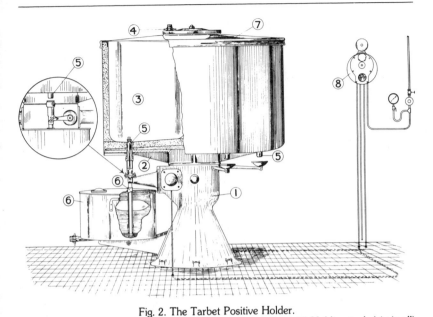

Fig. 2. The Tarbet Positive Holder.
(1) Pedestal with rotating mechanism (2) Supporting platform (3) Holding tank (six in all) (4) Milk inlet (5) Milk outlet (6) Discharge pipe and receiver (7) Cover (8) Controller.

external mechanism after the holding period was complete (Fig. 2). His suggestion was made on 3 November. Seligman grasped its significance at once and acted with great alacrity. On the ninth a patent application in the names of Tarbet and the company was approved and it was filed the following day. A prototype was made up and tested by 21 December and on the next day was demonstrated to an appreciative audience of leading dairymen.

The Tarbet holder was at once put on the market. It was an immediate success. It was made in a series of standard capacities from 125 to 1,000 gallons per hour and by September 1923 twenty-five plants were in use.

So one half of the problem of designing a fully satisfactory milk pasteurisation plant was solved. The other, the devising of a suitable heating and cooling plant remained. On 23 December, the day after the successful demonstration of the Tarbet Holder, Seligman left for a family ski-ing holiday at Lenzerheide, announcing to his colleagues his intention to invent a heater to go with it whilst he was away.

There followed a remarkable episode. Seligman who, as he admitted himself, had no familiarity with the principles of heat transfer, took with him on his holiday two books on the subject. All day long was spent with his family in the sunshine, climbing the mountains and enjoying his favourite relaxation, ski-ing. In the evening after dinner in the one public room of the hotel, while the family danced or played games, Seligman pored over his tomes. After a few evenings, reading gave place to scribbled calculations and then to rough sketches. He had, in principle, solved his problem. The idea of the plate heat exchanger, at least in its original form, had been evolved.

The circumstances were certainly favourable to innovative invention. The market demand was obvious. The technical requirement was equally clear to him: a heater of reasonably high efficiency and of hygienic construction in a material that would neither contaminate, nor be attacked by milk; compact yet accessible for cleaning; capable of being used for regenerative heating and cooling; and with some positive means of preventing contamination of treated milk with untreated milk, an essential if the decisive feature of the Tarbet Holder was not to be thrown away.

The existing machine nearest to meeting these requirements was the Wisner double tube. Seligman saw that, if the tubes could be split in two, they could be readily inspected and cleaned. If the split tubes could be folded to and fro on themselves, the space required would be greatly reduced. At that point came the inventive flash. What if, instead of tubes, zig-zag channels were formed in rectangular cast plates connected to ports at the corners, one set of channels isolated from another by rubber cord gaskets fitted in grooves machined at the edge of the plates, all clamped together as in a filter press? Would this not meet the criteria with one liquid flowing through one set of channels and the other through the alternate ones in counter-current? Then, by blanking off some of the feed ports, any arrangement of plates in series or in parallel could be made to suit the duty. Other liquids, too, could be introduced into, or removed from, the machine so that regenerative heating, final heating and cooling could all be carried out in a single frame. And lastly, if the space enclosed between the gaskets isolating the flow passages of the two liquids was vented to the atmosphere through a 'leakage groove' then contamination by adventitious leakage between the two would be positively prevented. The problem was solved and the plate heat exchanger invented.

Seligman's notebook has disappeared but a reproduction of three key pages of sketches and calculations has survived (Fig. 3). It shows how the idea first took shape. The calculations are purely dimensional of a plate with groove area equivalent to a pair of 1½-inch tubes ten feet long. No calculation of heat transfer coefficient, Reynolds number or the other parameters that we would expect nowadays.

The sketches were sent back to Wandsworth and development work started in earnest. A mock-up series of plates made up from sheet copper were ready almost as soon as Seligman got back from Switzerland. They were tested out by Percy Williams in the little shed that now served as test house. Satisfactory results were obtained and designs of the machine in a usable form worked out.

This consisted of tinned cast-gunmetal plates of two configurations, the so-called combined and water plates. The combined plate was not only grooved on both sides but had cavities in between through which a second liquid could pass; the water plate was grooved on one side only. The plates were accommodated in the frame of a little filter press borrowed for the purpose.

By May 1923, a prototype had been made up (Illustration 27) and was tested in a dairy quite close to the Wandsworth works. It gave precisely the results required and was demonstrated to E. A. Shepheard, then Chief Engineer to United Dairies Ltd. It was obviously necessary to get the backing of a large dairy concern if the machine was to be marketed effectively in the industry.

49

Plate Heat Exchanger

The first machine to be designed is a simple Milk Heater i.e. one in which the Milk is to be heated by hot water.

I desire to heat the Milk to 150°F from 50°F with water as low in temp. as possible & not exceeding 20° above the final temp of the Milk which in practice will probably be 147°F.

I should like each single plate to do 100g. per hr. — on thereabout with a margin. The amount of water is only limited by practical considerations i.e. power required to pump it but should obviously be as small as possible.

For this purpose it seems to me that two types of plate will be required & that together they will give a complete range

over.

Fig. 3. Pages from Richard Seligman's note book showing calculations and sketches of his first plate heat exchanger (January 1923).

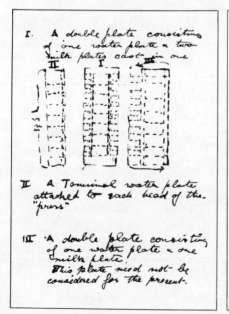

I. A double plate consisting of one water plate & two milk plates cast in one

II. A Terminal water plate attached to each head of the "press"

III. A double plate consisting of one water plate & one milk plate. This plate need not be considered for the present.

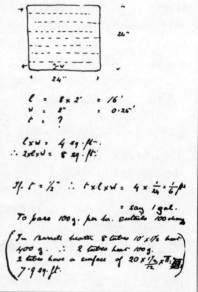

$l = 8 \times 2' = 16'$
$w = 8'' = 0.25'$
$t = ?$

$l \times w = 4 \, sq. ft.$
$\therefore 2 \times l \times w = 8 \, sq. ft.$

If $t = \frac{1}{2}'' \therefore t \times l \times w = 4 \times \frac{1}{24} = \frac{1}{6} ft.$

= say 1 gal.
To pass 100g. per hr. entails 100 changes

(In Barrell heater 8 tubes 10' x 1½ heat 400 g. ∴ 2 tubes heat 100 g. 2 tubes have a surface of 20 x ½ x π = 7·9 sq. ft.

50

Fortunately, Shepheard immediately perceived the possibilities of the new machine and gave permission to try out a full-sized installation at the Aylesbury Dairy Company's plant in Bayswater. This was designed for a complete range of duties, including the so-called HTST (high temperature, short time) process for pasteurisation using 165°F (73.9°C) for four seconds. By the autumn of 1923, it was in service most successfully. The plate heat exchanger was a commercial reality.

The development had been carried through with remarkable speed and efficiency. Besides Williams, W. E. Crosby had been largely responsible for technical development and design. On the manufacturing side, Ted Whitlock and others had contributed much. The company was beginning to benefit from the team of able people that Seligman was building up about him although he was the undisputed leader.

The advent of the plate heat exchanger represented perhaps the major landmark in the history of the company. Its business was transformed by it; to what extent and with what ramifications its inventor could not possibly have foreseen.

## Chapter 5

# The Plate Heat Exchanger
# 1923–1933

The next decade saw a complete transformation in the company. With the advent of the plate heat exchanger the business could never be the same again. It changed from one of metallurgical engineers primarily involved with the construction of vessels, to one of process engineers supplying complete plant lines, even equipping complete factories in which fabrication work, however important, played only a subsidiary part. As so often, Richard Seligman hit on the right phrase: 'Our job is to supply machines with brains.' And so it has remained.

Production expanded, not only in volume but also in kind. The machine shop and foundry became as integral a part of the company as the coppersmiths' shop. The demands for space intensified as did those for management and development skills. It was a time of extraordinarily fast expansion in turnover, in ideas, in personnel and in markets. As such, it brought new stresses as well as greatly increased profits.

The plate heat exchanger was immediately put on the market in the dairy industry along with the Tarbet Holder. In its original form, with two types of cast plate, it must have been horribly difficult to produce.

It was not long before improvements were introduced. In about 1924 W. E. Crosby devised the plate which, like all the others, was made of cast and tinned gunmetal (a tin-zinc bronze) with passages machined into both sides and a tinned copper sheet metal plate fitted between each pair (Illustration 9). Thus one type of plate could be used for all duties. It was also more flexible and allowed an appreciably improved heat transfer. It was introduced in 1925 and it eventually became the only type of plate used in the machine designated the HER.

Crosby was now Seligman's Development Engineer and the HER was the first of several ideas of his which were of great service to the company. He was a reserved, rather dour individual of much greater imagination than would have been expected on first acquaintance, who had joined the company at the beginning of 1917 as a draughtsman.

By 1925 the HER was virtually in the form it was to retain over its long working life. It was on the market for some twenty-five years or so until 1948, but many machines ran much longer than that.

Attempts to get adequate patent protection for the new heat exchanger, however, were running into difficulties. Seligman's invention had involved, for him, entirely novel mental processes but, when it came to trying to patent the machine, it was found that practically every feature, new though it had appeared, had been anticipated and previously patented, some nearly half a century before, although none had found any notable commercial application and none combined all the features in one machine. But no-one else had thought of the little leakage groove between the gaskets that prevented contamination of one liquid by leakage from another. This became the one indubitably patentable feature of the invention, an essential one because of the link with the basic feature of the Tarbet Holder.

Whether because of these difficulties or because the value of the new machine was underestimated or because of ignorance of the complexities of international patent law, the overseas patents taken out were quite insufficient. Broadly speaking wherever the HER was not patented it was copied, though with almost no understanding of the fundamentals involved.

The effect was greatest in export markets. At the beginning of 1928 Wilson reported to the Board on these difficulties and it was agreed to try to supply plates manufactured in Wandsworth 'through firms with whom the company worked in close collaboration'.

Not unnaturally, seeing the weakness of the patent position, several foreign competitors made efforts to sell in Britain and action had to be taken to combat them.

Nor was it only overseas competitors that had to be dealt with. Arthur G. Enock & Co. Ltd (later Graham Enock), a well-known firm of dairy engineers, had filed a patent for a holding device exactly on the same principle as Tarbet's but in which the tanks remained stationary and the filling and discharging mechanism revolved. By a strange coincidence this was filed just one day before the Tarbet Holder was first demonstrated in December 1922. Both firms lodged oppositions to the other's patents but common sense prevailed and agreement was reached without having to go to law.

The combination of the plate heat exchanger with the Tarbet Holder in effect produced a pasteurising plant that was better than anything else available at that time. Moreover, just as the plate machine was being tested, the Milk (Special Designations) Order 1923 was drawn up and finally revised in Seligman's own library in Lincoln House on Wimbledon Parkside. It specified the conditions for producing 'pasteurised milk' in this country – a holding period of thirty minutes at a temperature of not less than 145°F (62.8°C) nor more than 150°F (65.6°C) and subsequent cooling to 50°F (10°C). This did not make pasteurisation mandatory by law – strictly speaking it only specified the conditions of treatment that had to be met for milk to be called 'pasteurised' – but in practice it did so. Plants began to be installed up and down the country.

Many of these were quite small. The days of amalgamation and the giant concern had not yet arrived. There were a lot of little dairies, especially those run by local co-operative societies. For these the Tarbet Holder was amply sufficient.

This too was developed and improved. The holder was made in a series of standard sizes for throughputs up to 800 gallons per hour or just over.

A number of the bigger city dairies, however, required plants larger than the Tarbet could handle. It was hardly practicable to put in a set of several units so further development work was undertaken.

In October 1923, E. A. Shepheard, Chief Engineer of United Dairies, patented a system whereby the milk was drawn through the heating sections of a heat exchanger into one of a series of tanks held under vacuum, kept there for the required pasteurising time and then discharged through the cooling sections to a receiving tank also held under vacuum. Although feasible in principle, Shepheard's patent gives no idea how the process could be carried out in practice other than by the operation of a quite impracticable system of valve movements.

A month or two later and, as it appears, quite independently, Seligman patented a similar process in which the holding tanks were fed, as in Shepheard's patent, by heated milk drawn into them under vacuum but were discharged under air pressure through the regenerative and cooling sections, thus completely eliminating by pressure difference any chance of contaminating treated with untreated milk. He also, in the same patent, covered a form of multi-port rotary valve that enabled the whole process to be operated simply and automatically by controlling not the flow of milk but the application of vacuum and pressure to the tanks in timed sequence.

Seligman acknowledged the priority of Shepheard's patent, obtained the rights to it and marketed it as the APV Vacuum Pasteurisation Process (Shepheard's patent). The first plant was installed at London Wholesale Dairies, Harrow Road, a plant belonging to United Dairies who again showed their courage in backing a new development. This was in 1925. The plant was highly successful and was soon designed to cover throughputs up to 6,000 gallons per hour. It was especially attractive as it eliminated pumps and could be run completely automatically. Eventually it was also manufactured in whole or in part in Canada, Germany, Italy and the United States under licence.

The basic idea may have been Shepheard's but the plant was Seligman's. A comparison of the two patents exemplifies the difference between a simple inventive idea and the practical form of the same concept. It illustrates, too, Seligman's remarkable ability to envisage a complete process together with the plant to operate it in concrete form and to apply his inventive ability to the parts needed to make it a practical commercial proposition, in this case the rotary valve that is the heart of the process.

The plate heat exchanger combined with the Tarbet or Shepheard vacuum holders enabled the pasteurising conditions demanded in the United Kingdom to be met very satisfactorily but in many other countries (and, since 1941, in the United Kingdom, too) the so-called HTST (high temperature, short time) process was used for pasteurisation. The actual times and temperatures varied substantially but might be, for instance, a temperature of 161°F (71.7°C) held for fifteen seconds. With considerable foresight, Seligman's first commercial trials of his plate heat exchanger at the Aylesbury Dairy Company had been carried out on an HTST process. It was therefore established that the plate heat exchanger was suitable for all milk pasteurisation duties and it quickly became the standard equipment all over the world. In its various modifications, whether manufactured by APV[1] or not, it has remained so ever since. As the instrument to carry out the prime object of its inventor it has been a triumphant success.

Milk pasteurisation lines involved the development of other plant and techniques. By 1927 a simple pedestal duplex cloth filter for milk was on the market, another of Seligman's patents. A whole new range of tanks, vertical and horizontal, insulated and bare, circular and rectangular, but all in aluminium, were developed. These were of much more sophisticated design than the earlier

[1]Although it was to be over twenty years before the company's name was formally altered from the Aluminium Plant and Vessel Company Limited to The A.P.V. Company Limited, the company was already referred to as 'APV' quite commonly and the initials were being used in much of the firm's publicity.

56

ranges. Aluminium churn tipping and weighing tanks were marketed, so that within a year or two from the invention of the heat exchanger, the company was in a position to install virtually complete dairy processing lines.

Because aluminium and, to a lesser extent, tinned copper are heavily attacked by alkalis, it was necessary to develop special detergents inhibited against corrosive action to remove the deposits that inevitably formed on the heated surfaces of a pasteurisation plant. This policy of investigating and devising cleaning and sterilising compounds and procedures that would avoid serious corrosion damage to APV plant was to remain a key one at least for another thirty or forty years.

Other uses of the heat exchanger were soon found. In the milk industry, cheese and butter-milk pasteurisers were developed and sold mainly in Holland, but the greatest expansion came in breweries. The first and most obvious application was to wort cooling. The open coolers used up to that time were costly, inefficient and insanitary. The Paraflow (as it was now being called even so early in its career) overcame this and allowed preheating of brewing liquor into the bargain. Tests were complicated by the large number of factors, aeration, colour, flavour, flocculation as well as thermal and bacterial effectiveness, that had to be investigated. Moritz' influence was of great help in dealing with these. After a year of trials the machine could be claimed to be a complete success on all counts. By autumn 1925, Paraflow wort coolers were working in seven British breweries; in 1930 over a hundred machines were in use; by 1935 they had found application in Europe, in Australia, New Zealand, India, South Africa and Canada and could be hailed as the first piece of brewery equipment exported from this country; and now they are almost universally used for this duty. Only Germany and the United States with their ultra-conservative Teutonic brewing traditions took time to convince.

Other applications in breweries were soon found. Following

experiments in conjunction with Moritz at Fuller, Smith and Turner's brewery in Chiswick, Seligman published in 1929 a paper on the Pasteurisation of Black Beers. In this he showed that treatment at 160°F (71.1°C) for about twelve seconds would provide to all intents and purposes a sterile beer without affecting its flavour. In addition the beer could be carbonated by injection of $CO_2$ into the beer stream in the heat exchanger. Because no means of sterile filling was available, the process was applied in the main only to tank bottoms and returned beers that might otherwise have been destroyed. It was not until the advent of keg beers some thirty years later that the process really came into its own.

Many other applications were to follow in later years, but one other development of the plate principle must be mentioned, not for its commercial importance at this time, but because of its further expansion many years later.

In mid-1930, Seligman patented the first plate evaporator. His imagination had been fired by the idea of the plate form of construction and he looked for other applications. This consisted of a series of cast-aluminium plates with vertical tube-like channels defined by ribs cast in them on one side and with large vapour and feed ports at the top and bottom. These alternated with steam heated channels, all clamped together in a frame thus forming in essence a dismountable short vertical tube calandria. It operated quite satisfactorily. Only one plant was sold (to Robertson's for marmalade) at the time, however, for the advantages over conventional plants were not so great as to gain it general acceptance. Actually, Robertson's ordered a repeat installation about twenty years later, but the full development of the plate evaporator was still to come, even then.

The APV process plants being installed in dairies and breweries required complex pipework that had to be readily dismountable for cleaning. There was a similar requirement for control cocks that had to be as far as possible leakproof. There were no suitable fittings on the market, and the company had to design its own.

Towards the end of 1927 Crosby patented his ring joint (later RJT) type of fitting and a leakproof plug cock. At this time these were made of gunmetal, tinned or not as necessary, and soldered or brazed to copper pipe.

In principle this type of cock and fitting became the basis of the company's large fittings business. They found application all over the world and are widely used to this day.

More and more the company was having to consider fabrication in metals other than aluminium. At that time by far the most important and widely used non-ferrous metal was copper. It, too, like aluminium twenty years earlier, suffered, though not so seriously, from the unsatisfactory methods of joining then available. Riveting, soldering and brazing were reasonably satisfactory mechanically but had serious drawbacks in corrosion resistance.

In 1922 Ted Whitlock, who was then in charge of outside work, visited Carl Canzler's works in Düren in the Rhineland, saw copper welded there and brought samples back with him together with some of the special filler rods that were used in gas welding at Düren. Experiments were started immediately using rods from Canzler but without success. Investigation, involving Percy Williams as well as Seligman himself, ultimately revealed that the copper sheet in use in those days was not suitable for welding. If, however, a deoxidant such as phosphorus or silicon were added to the base metal, then the difficulty was overcome. The Metals Division of ICI, formed only a year or two before, eventually produced suitable deoxidised sheet, agreement was reached with Canzler to supply welding rods under licence, and, in 1925, APV became the first British firm to weld copper.

The new process was applied to the manufacture of fermenting vessels, varnish pots, copper pipework and so on but, much more important, it led directly to a technological development that was to have a considerable effect on the company's development.

Just about this time, Ralph came back from his job as general salesman in the North to take over from C. A. Wyatt as chemical and general representative at Wandsworth.

The organic chemical industry at that time was based essentially on coal tar and alcohol as feedstocks. Our modern petrochemical industry was not developed until the 1950s. The alcohol was obtained by fermentation of molasses and concentrated and purified in large complex distillation plants all, for the most part, fabricated in copper. Solvent recovery in a number of industries also involved large distillation plants. Cellulose acetate production required large acetic acid extraction and recovery plants. These and many of the processes for producing other organic chemicals included distillation plant, for the most part of copper; suitable stainless steels had not been invented.

Ralph saw the opportunity that copper welding had given him and approached the main firms involved. The Distillers Company (DCL) had, and maintained, a virtual monopoly in the production of industrial alcohol. Through their chemical subsidiaries, which were just being set up at this time, they manufactured many of the chemicals derived from it. British Celanese at Spondon was at first the sole producer of cellulose acetate but Courtaulds also started production at Coventry in 1928. Glover, the Technical Director of Courtaulds at the time, had been a colleague of Ralph's working under Mendola at Finsbury Technical College.

Ralph was therefore well placed, especially as in this country there was no specialist firm in the type of distillation plant required. Columns were mostly obtained from France and Germany. As a result, at the behest of DCL and Courtaulds, APV equipped themselves to manufacture large distillation columns.

A number of what were then very large plants were supplied, manufactured to drawings provided by the customer. The costing and manufacture of these were something of a gamble for which special provision had to be made, but they worked and APV was established in the distillation business that was to be so important in later years.

In the varnish trade there were also developments. There were obvious advantages in producing boiled oil in a closed circuit rather than open pots and at the beginning of 1930 an agreement was reached with Heinrich Sommer Nachfolger of Düsseldorf to market their oil boiling and ester gum plants while they acted as technical consultants to APV. As a result the varnish business expanded rapidly with the ability to put down complete plants and generally larger and more complex installations.

With all this new development going on, the old standard lines continued steadily and were in their turn also improved.

With transport tanks the improvements were marked indeed. Because of their lighter weight and consequent greater carrying capacity for a given chassis load, aluminium was finding favour over steel for transporting oil products as well as for beer and milk. In 1930, Crosby (once more) devised a much lighter and simpler mounting. These, combined with a new tank designed to take full advantage of the mounting, allowed still greater weight savings and put APV ahead of its competitors of which a number had emerged now that the Schoop patents had expired.

The sales started to climb and by 1931 it was decided to establish a transport tank department that was to provide substantial turnover for some thirty years.

There was substantial expansion of food plant business, particularly in a series of jacketed pans where improvements were made both by patented designs and in welded manufacture so extending the range to copper, nickel, monel and eventually stainless steel. This was to be a lucrative line for many years.

Foundry work had become of much greater importance to the company as a result of the development of heat exchanger plates, yeast presses, transport tank mountings and cocks and fittings, almost all in either gunmetal or Alpax (aluminium-silicon alloy). A large proportion of its turnover, however, was still sold to outside firms. Alpax, a light alloy of excellent properties but requiring some skill in melting and casting, had been developed in about 1923. A

61

licence was acquired and it became standard production at APV. By 1930, the foundry had an impressive record of quite big and complicated castings, especially for chemical engineering duties.

The foundry also produced some proprietary products of their own. They marketed a series of excellent Alpax ham, meat and brisket moulds that had a wide sale for many years.

The expansion of APV's business, not only in volume but also in kind, demanded radical changes in marketing organisation and methods. Not until mid-1925, however, was the decision taken to appoint a 'traveller' to deal solely with the sale of dairy plant. C. A. Wyatt was given the job.

The dairy business continued to expand and other salesmen were needed in what was now the Dairy Engineering Department. An early recruit was J. S. ('Jock') Menzies, a highly extrovert Scot who devoted his life to selling APV plant. Much of the liquid milk supply of the country was processed and distributed through local co-operative societies. Some of these were large but most, especially in the smaller towns, were comparatively small and quite unsophisticated technically. Jock Menzies became a specialist in selling to this market and virtually cornered it. He was not gifted as a technologist and he was the bane of those who tried to keep him organised in the office but he was a salesman of genius with a core of hard common sense. His market required, and got from him, a special personal approach.

The biggest change in marketing, however, came overseas. The plate heat exchanger and its auxiliaries gave the company a chance to export for the first time and the chance was taken.

APV's first agent was taken on somewhat melodramatically. A stocky Dutchman named Merkens strode on to the APV stand at the Dairy Show in the Royal Agricultural Hall, Islington, in February 1926 and bluntly informed Seligman and Wilson that he had decided to sell the APV products in Holland. Agreement was soon reached and, although there was no written document, the association lasted until Merkens' death and continues in the group subsidiary, APV Nederland, whose Managing Director is Wim Merkens, his son.

Until this encounter, no plans had been made for selling abroad; the dairy engineering industry was, at that time, so dominated by continental and American firms that the possibility had not been considered.

Merkens worked on his own from his home in Amersfoort but he had engineering training, a knowledge of English and the imagination to see the potential of the heat exchanger. The first installation in 1926 was an HER machine with Tarbet Holder in the VAMI dairy in Amsterdam, and many installations followed.

In the United States an agreement was made at the beginning of 1927 with the York Milk Machinery Company to manufacture, sell and use plate heat exchangers under the APV US patents. This connection continued until after the 1939–45 war. There was a further agreement early in 1930 with the Pfaudler Company of Rochester, New York, to manufacture under the Shepheard patents.

Another licence to manufacture was negotiated with Holstein und Kappert of Dortmund, Germany, for fifteen years from October 1927. Thus started a long, if somewhat stormy, relationship that has lasted to this day. Even then, there were some troubles for in 1932 sales were made by H&K to Russia through Berlin and accordingly claimed as German sales.

In 1926, John Bryant of Bryant Brothers in Sydney, Australia, was on a visit to this country and saw an APV heat exchanger at work. As a result he agreed to prospect the Australian market for APV products. Early in the following year the first sale was made, a 1,000 gallon per hour cream pasteuriser to Gladstone, Queensland. Thus started, again informally, another long association that continues in the group subsidiary company, Bell-Bryant Ltd. With his wide knowledge of the dairy and engineering industries, John Bryant acted both as consultant and spur until his death in 1974.

The next agent to be appointed was Rigamonti of Milan. His great achievement was the sale to the, for those days, very large Milan

Central City Dairy consisting of a vacuum pressure holder plant with a throughput of 25,000 litres per hour (5,500 gph) that was the company's showpiece of this period (Illustration 10).

AB Separator (Alfa-Laval) was appointed agent for Sweden, Norway and Finland for a period of ten years. It is curious that the first appearance in this history of APV's major competitor world-wide should be as the company's agent.

By now, the export business and its ramifications had become such that in May 1929 the Board decided to appoint a Foreign Sales Manager. In September it was decided to appoint Raymond Thomas. It was an excellent choice. Seligman had known him since his days in Zürich where Thomas was reading electrical engineering and he had twenty-five years technical selling in a number of countries behind him. He was a bachelor, a typical Englishman of the old school with a passion for salmon fishing and the kindest of hearts who made friends wherever he went.

The first fruit of his appointment was the engagement of Walker-Wallace of Toronto as agents for Canada for six years from the beginning of 1930. K. L. Wallace was the Managing Director and principal shareholder in the firm. The association proved a very successful one and is continued to this day in APV-Crepaco of Canada and A.P.V. Company Incorporated in Tonawanda, USA, both of which derive, in part at least, directly from Walker-Wallace.

With all this new commercial development, turnover and profits increased dramatically. In 1924 the turnover was about £116,400 with a profit of £9,400 somewhat depressed by the high development costs. Over the next few years, sales rose steadily until 1929 when they reached a peak of £272,400 with a profit of £31,100. That year the great slump came but, with its new products, APV weathered the storm very well. Over the years 1930 to 1933 the turnover averaged about £245,000 and the profit about £22,500 except in 1933, another year of very high development expenditure.

The total dividend paid per annum was 10% free of tax and each year except 1928 and 1932, an extra bonus of 5%, also free of tax. The fair value of the shares rose from £1 4s (£1.20) in 1923 to £2 in 1928 and then was set at a dizzy £3 4s (£3.20) in 1929. For the years afterwards to 1933 it was reduced to £2 10s (£2.50).

During this time, the balance of licence royalty payments was completely reversed. Over the period 1923 to 1926, an average of nearly £700 per annum had been paid out in royalties to AAS, Zürich. Then agreement was reached at the end of 1927 to commute the annual royalties by payment of £2,500. After this no more payments were made to the Swiss. But in 1931, licence payments began to come in from the manufacturing agreements in the United States and Germany, rising to £1,360 in 1933.

Not surprisingly, the expansion of turnover to just about double in five years and its maintenance there through a period of severe slump, caught the Board rather unawares. In early 1924, there was clearly some fear that resources might be overstretched if development was not curtailed and the position with the new products consolidated. Wilson was particularly worried at the costs involved in the export business. There was concern, too, at what might happen if the new dairy business fell away. To their credit, however, the Board imposed no restraints, technical or marketing.

The only change in the Board, though an important one, was occasioned by the death of Dr Moritz after a long illness. His last attendance was in July 1930. On 18 November 1931, Seligman was elected Chairman. In January 1933, half Moritz' shares were allotted to his nephew, F. E. B. ('Tam') Moritz, also a brewery consultant, who was appointed to the Board at the end of March.

At about this time divergences of opinion began to appear on the Board, more especially between Seligman and Wilson that were to lead to a serious split ten years later.

Wilson and Seligman had been personal friends long before Wilson joined the Board, but they were very different in outlook and temperament. For a long time they regarded themselves as a good team with Seligman responsible for all technical matters including those involved in production while Wilson looked after sales and administration. As time went by, however, it seemed to Seligman that Wilson was becoming less and less capable of handling a business that was getting almost daily more complex as well as bigger.

From correspondence between the two early in 1933, the difference in attitudes becomes clear. Wilson's approach was essentially a straightforward one; if it were profitable to dispose of the business, he would not hesitate to do so. He regarded the form of the business as simply a reflection of Seligman's personality and abilities and therefore one that could only be carried on if Seligman, or at least a technical staff of similar outlook, were employed in it. In this, his outlook was a blinkered one. He did not allow for the natural evolution of an industrial organism.

Not so Seligman. He wanted 'to establish an organism which has the seed of life in it, which will go on after my departure or death with somewhat the same ideals as have actuated me and which will prove a suitable field of activity for those of my kin and friends who may share in it.'

The position was not made any easier by Seligman's rather intolerant attitude, often sharply expressed, to what he considered were Wilson's inadequacies. Nor by Wilson's ill-judged, if understandable, appeals to personal friendship. It was inevitable that a clash should develop.

With the expansion of the business there was a corresponding expansion of staff. The total number of employees, 175 in 1924, rose to 340 in 1929 and 420 in 1934.

The most important new appointment was that of Ted Whitlock as Works Manager in 1924, a post he held for over 20 years. He was a brilliant coppersmith and a man of volatile temperament with something of the artful dodger in his make-up. He was a trades union socialist of the old school and for many years was a Wandsworth Borough councillor and eventually an Alderman. He managed the growing works well and filled what had been a serious

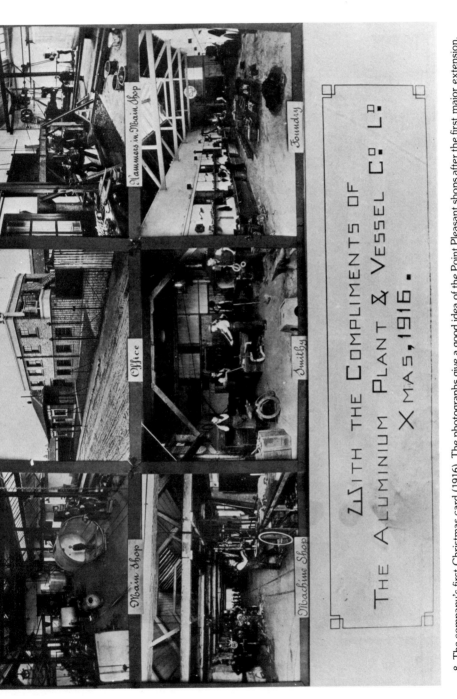

With the Compliments of
The Aluminium Plant & Vessel Co. Ld.
Xmas, 1916.

Hammers in Main Shop

Foundry

Office

Smithy

Main Shop

Machine Shop

8. The company's first Christmas card (1916). The photographs give a good idea of the Point Pleasant shops after the first major extension.

9. (Left) HER plate heat excha
The developed form of the ori
machine (1925).

10. (Centre) The process room
Milan Central Dairy, APV's firs
complete overseas contract (1

11. (Below) A stainless steel 'Syr
plant with HS heat exchanger
filter at Swindon (1938).

*Facing page:*
12. (Above) Percy Williams, Chi
Chemist, in his 'new' laboratory
(1928).

13. (Below) The APV Company
Board (1935). From left to right
Gerald Seligman, Richard Seligm
J. W. Wilson, Tam Moritz.

14. A conference in the Northfields boardroom (1955). From left to right: Madron Seligman, Richard Seligman, Hugh Goodman, Jack Matthews, Tony Dummett, Peter Seligman. (The Chairman's chair bore the extraordinary inscription: 'Woman in love an angel is: unloving she should never live.')

15. Sir Peter Seligman, CBE, Managing Director of The A.P.V. Company Ltd. 1947 to 1968; Chairman 1965 to 1977.

gap in the company's management ever since it was founded.

On the engineering side there were also important changes. T. E. French was Chief Draughtsman, a rather pedantic and dapper little man, but a more competent engineer than might have been expected from first impressions. In 1926 there were only six draughtsmen under him.

At the end of 1929, Seligman reported the need for another design engineer and a metallurgist to deal with the growing technical load. The Board agreed and H. W. G. Hignett, an excellent metallurgist of great, sometimes wild, imagination was appointed. He soon became a remarkable founding and welding specialist and set the pattern for the series of gifted metallurgists that have served the company since then.

The engineer appointment took a different turn. Actually the firm had already, in 1928, appointed the design engineer it needed, H. F. Goodman, who was then working under Crosby. However, it was decided also to appoint an engineering adviser to the Board with the intention that he should become Technical Director and take some of the load off Seligman's shoulders. At the end of 1933, Dr Aubrey Burstall, a mechanical engineer from ICI, was engaged. It was to prove a disastrous move and Burstall left a year or two later.

Actually this was of no great importance. Burstall had not shown nor, perhaps, been allowed to show any ability to don Seligman's mantle. Seligman remained the undisputed leader of a team that now included Goodman and Hignett, and later others, as well as Crosby and Williams. Although he took an active part in all technical matters himself, he was beginning to rely more and more on his colleagues.

As long as he was Chairman, he made a point of visiting his technical staff every day if possible, rather like a Professor doing the rounds of his research students. There were discussions at the bench or over the board, suggestions made and decisions taken but, from this point on, all the innovations and improvements (and they were many) introduced under his direction were increasingly the result of teamwork.

The hours worked naturally followed the turnover more or less closely with an average output of 10s (50p) per productive hour worked. The average wage worked out at 1s 7d to 1s 10d (8p to 9p) per hour. This was about 1½d above the normal rate in industry.

Whitlock had a deep appreciation of the importance of apprentice training. One of his first acts as Works Manager was to set up a formal scheme. Among the apprentice indentures recorded at this time are several old coppersmith family names, Harlock, Freeman and Talman amongst them.

Employees' welfare was not neglected. There was now a week's holiday with pay. In 1927 the Board agreed to a bonus to be paid to certain selected members of staff for their work in the previous year and to be deducted from the profits for 1926. From then on a staff bonus was paid amounting to some 10% to 15% of the profit before tax.

At the end of 1927, the Board decided to set up a Staff Benefit and Pension Fund. Eventually, in mid-1932, a Trust Fund was set up with Seligman and Wilson as trustees. This was to provide a benefit fund and £1,000 per annum was paid in yearly from profits.

Apparently, the original Athletic and Social Club must have fallen into decay because in 1928 a few APV employees got together with the idea of forming a sports club. They persuaded others to subscribe 2s 6d (12½p) per annum and collected some equipment for a football and a cricket team. By 1931, they had reached the premier division of the Wimbledon league. This was the true start of the present flourishing club.

The expansion of the business once more demanded increased space. In October 1925, Wilson proposed a far-reaching scheme of demolition and rebuilding to be financed from revenue and a bank overdraft. This, however, proved too ambitious. A year or two later the die foundry had gone, extensions were being made to the machine shop and the new works offices were being built. In addition new machinery and fittings were supplied for the machine, press, blacksmiths' and coppersmiths' shops as well as the test house; new roads and gates were supplied and a cottage transformed into a laboratory (Illustration 12). This was all going to cost £13,000, some of it being charged to revenue and some to capital account, in 1926 and 1927.

At the end of 1928, the foundry was proving quite inadequate. A night shift had had to be worked for the previous two years and the operation was becoming uneconomical. In May 1928 it was decided to build a new foundry in the garden behind Northfields House and to put a new shop in the space occupied by the old foundry. The new one went to work in mid-1930. The drain on resources was such that the Board started considering ways of increasing capital. Nevertheless, with further extensions in mind, in spring 1930 the Board authorised the purchase of twenty-six cottages in Point Pleasant. Immediately plans were made for further building of a stores and laboratory at the Point Pleasant entrance to the works. At the same time extensions were made to the existing shops. All of this was finished by the end of 1931.

Finally, towards the end of 1932, Wilson, with some hesitation, presented a case for finally pulling down the remnants of the old shops and building a new one to be used as an extension of the fabricating facilities including stainless steel. The Board agreed to proceed.

Some alterations to the offices also took place. A 'temporary hut' for use as a drawing office was put up adjoining Northfields House. It was a peculiarly dingy contraption and those who experienced the extraordinary combination of gloom, fug and tobacco smoke will never forget it. How any work was done there is a mystery.

By the end of the period a very remarkable development was taking place. For some years, ever since Brearley had produced the first cast of chromium steel in 1913, Seligman had been looking for the advent of weldable stainless steels. It was not until 1924, however, that the first cast was made at Firth's Sheffield works of an 18/8 chrome-nickel stainless steel more or less as we know it. This could be rolled to sheet, would take a high finish, had excellent mechanical properties and, as rolled, high corrosion resistance. It had what would now be regarded as a high carbon content so, although it could readily be shaped, it was liable, when welded, to the catastrophic corrosive attack known as 'weld decay'.

Only in 1929 did Krupp in Germany file their first patent covering the addition of titanium in small amounts as a stabiliser to stainless steels whereby weld decay was finally conquered.

By 1931 weldable material became available in this country and the possibility of supplying welded stainless steel vessels became a real one.

The gas welding process used for alumunium and copper was not suitable for stainless steel. Electric arc welding, for which suitable electrodes were becoming available, was better and more economic. Accordingly the process was introduced to Wandsworth in 1931, not without difficulties that could only be overcome by an extended training programme.

At first the process was used for mild steel only but quite soon the shops were turning out a variety of vessels and equipment in the stabilised stainless material.

This was not the only change in manufacturing methods brought about by the use of stainless steel. APV had always set itself a high standard of finish in its fabrication work. Aluminium and copper welds could be hammered or rolled flat and very easily polished if need be. In any case, gas welding properly carried out gave a very neat weld. With the much harder stainless steel and the use of arc welding, the rougher weld needed grinding and then polishing to give a satisfactory finish. As a result, the skilled polisher became an essential part of the company's workforce.

The advantages offered by stainless steel over aluminium or copper for the fabrication of food plant were overwhelming: higher strength and rigidity, so the ability to fabricate in thin sheet; brilliant finish when polished; high corrosion resistance expecially to alkaline cleaning solutions; and a hard surface much less easily damaged than those of the non-ferrous metals. In the sheet form it was competitive in price with aluminium or tinned copper.

It was subject to three major drawbacks, however. Its thermal conductivity was low, much inferior to aluminium or copper; its resistance to pitting attack by acid chloride solutions, so often occurring in foodstuffs, was suspect and by cooling brines was, at that time, quite unacceptable. (Later the discovery of the effect of the addition of molybdenum on the resistance of stainless steels to chlorides was to alter this position completely.) Finally, castings in stainless steel were both difficult to produce and very costly. However desirable it might be to convert the plate heat exchanger directly to stainless steel, there were substantial impediments to so doing.

In fact, however, both licencees, York and Holstein und Kappert, did produce and sell modified forms of HER plate in stainless steel but neither was a great success.

To Seligman, it was clear that the plates of a new stainless steel machine must be made of thin sheet. Only thus could the low thermal conductivity be tolerated and cast construction obviated. Moreover, if a sound new patent could be obtained, then all the difficulties over copies of the HER, patent actions and the inherent weakness of the first patent could be put aside and he and the company reap a full reward for their undoubted innovations.

Seligman was also anxious to find a plate form in which increased heat transfer coefficients would help still further to overcome the effect of low thermal conductivity and reduce the surface area required, and in which the pressure drop for a given duty would also be reduced.

It was clear that the plate would have to be of the 'straight through flow' type and not of the channel type like the HER. Accordingly in 1932 a series of rather crude experiments were started by Percy Williams under Seligman's direction to determine whether, by creating a suitable path for the liquids between which heat was to be exchanged, the required increase in heat transfer could be obtained without so increasing the pressure drop as to

71

make the resulting machine uneconomic. Innumerable shapes were constructed, tested and abandoned.

It seemed like an impasse. Then, curiously like the tale of ten years earlier, Switzerland again played a part.

It was Seligman's habit to make the journey from Point Pleasant to Lincoln House on foot and to think over some of the problems of the day as he went. In the spring of 1933, these thoughts were gloomy for little or no progress with the investigation could be perceived. Then one evening his thoughts turned to a peasant's water trough in the Ticino which he had seen several years before and that had prompted thoughts about the 'venturi' effect of successive expansions and contractions. Could this be applied to the liquid as it flowed along the plate? The idea was discussed next morning with Goodman and it seemed so, if some form of closely nesting troughs was pressed into the plate. Goodman reported on a number of possibilities that included the form that was actually applied (Fig. 4). In this the spacing between the plates was reduced and simple troughs were pressed across them. The troughs of successive plates interlocked and so produced a series of horizontal chambers corresponding with the flat portions, separated by channels of much smaller cross-section defined by the steep walls of the troughs. The small spacing (about 4 mm) in itself tended to increase turbulence and therefore heat transfer which was then enhanced by the successive acceleration and deceleration of the fluid passing through the narrow corrugated passages. Rubber gaskets held in a surrounding frame defined the major chamber and the small spacing required between successive plates.

This basic idea was patented by Seligman in April 1933, but there were a great deal of further tests, of design work and of production engineering to be done before the idea could be translated into manufacturing reality. It was not until December that year that Seligman, Crosby and Goodman patented the precise form of plate that was to be used in the new range and APV was fully equipped to enter the era of stainless steel.

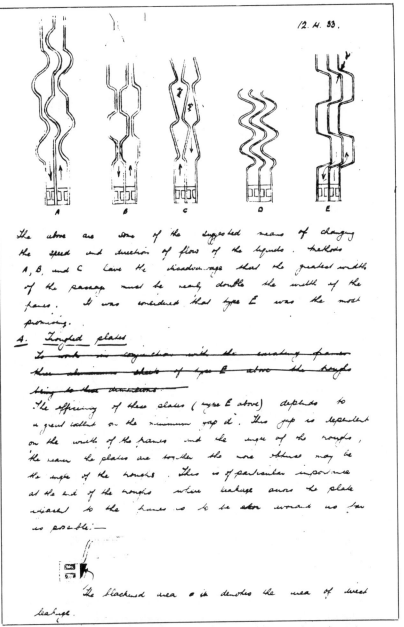

Fig. 4. Extract from High Goodman's report on various trough configurations incorporating the Venturi principle for pressed heat exchanger plates (April 1933). Form E was that finally used for HH, HL and HS plates.

## Chapter 6

# The Change to Stainless Steel
# 1934–1939

It was clear that the new design of heat exchanger had to be offered on the market as quickly as possible if full advantage was also to be gained from the use of stainless steel for tanks and other items of plant. Seligman recognised that this would not be a simple matter for, unlike the HER, new production methods not available in the company, as well as new design considerations, would be called for.

In January 1934, Seligman set before the Board his objectives in developing the new heat exchanger, told them of the difficulties experienced so far that had involved the, in those days, high cost of about £3,000 and warned them that it would cost as much again to get the machine into production. The Board not only accepted this unanimously but went on to reiterate its policy to 'look for its main source of profit to specialised technical plant for which [the company] should be able to get prices commensurate with the research and brainwork necessary to its development.'

The main factors that had to be decided were, first, the precise dimensions of the troughs. These were determined by small-scale heat transfer tests made with suitably shaped strips of metal, cross-sections of a plate as it were, in the new laboratory which was now located over the test house, next to the stores entrance in Point Pleasant.

Then came the size of plate which was estimated on the areas required to carry out the sort of milk pasteurisation duties that it was expected it would have to meet – 1,200 to 1,500 gallons per hour with 75% regeneration – tiny on present day standards. It was

74

also decided to have two sizes of plate with identical trough form but the smaller with half the area of the larger. The thickness had to be such that, with support from pressed pips in the plate, it was adequately rigid to support the not very large pressure differences to which it would be subjected.

This decided, there came the biggest problem of all. Before even a prototype could be made, plates had to be pressed and the company knew little or nothing about pressing sheet in any material, let alone the new stainless steels. Seligman and Whitlock went round the country to firms of press tool makers; all in vain. Seligman's typical comment was, 'We are back on our resources, where I would much rather be.' So. H. Hawkey, who had joined the firm as an apprentice only eight years before, designed the tools and calculated the forces needed to use them. Someone went to the East End of London and, after Hawkey had checked that it would stand the stresses, bought a second-hand press for £40. In three months plates were being produced, one trough being pressed after another in succession.

There was no question of pressing complex inlet distributors or gasket retaining grooves; that was too difficult. So inlet 'bridge' pieces were machined up and welded in under the open ports, while frames of beryllium copper spot-welded to the edge of the plates were used to define the rubber grooves (Fig. 5).

The rubbers, too, had to be specially designed for they had to withstand high loads for long periods, resist attack by both the liquids treated and the cleaning solutions, be non-toxic and non-corrosive to stainless steel, all at temperatures near boiling point. A great deal of work was done by Percy Williams in conjunction with the rubber companies to find the right formula.

Suitable steels for brine plates were not available so they were made in tinned copper. It was not until 1938 that molybdenum-bearing 18/8 stainless steels came on the market and solved the problem.

The frames were made with cast semi-steel ends and finished either in mottled blue-grey vitreous enamel or in white.

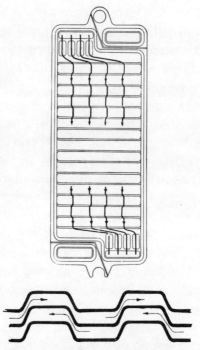

Fig. 5. HL plate in its original form.

The first frame of the larger plate, the HH, was fitted with hand-pumped hydraulic tightening. This was before its time and it gave a lot of trouble. In 1937 it was replaced by a simple hand-tightening frame, the HL, very similar to that used from the beginning for the smaller plate, the HS.

The necessary connector and holder plates were fabricated from stainless and mild steel with fittings of 'stainproof' (German silver), a nickel bronze, or tinned gunmetal.

Prototypes of both the HH and HS were shown in 1934 but it was not until there had been extended plant trials that the final versions were exhibited at the 1935 Dairy Show. Orders were immediately taken and both machines sold well from then on.

Sales were mainly in the dairy industry for which the machines were primarily designed. A few, however, were sold abroad mainly for fruit juice and wine for which they were particularly suitable.

There followed a lot of development to take advantage of stainless steel contact. Cleaned-up designs of storage, Tarbet and vacuum-pressure tanks; various forms of cream vats and batch pasteurisers were all put out in the new material. The cocks and brazed-on RJT fittings were marketed in German silver as well as gunmetal, and in 1937 Crosby patented a modified cock that was the forerunner of the present range. New stainless duplex filters to go with the HL and HS machines were also developed.

The Tarbet and Shepheard vacuum-pressure holder units continued to sell well as long as the holder process was required. By 1939, 107 Tarbet plants had been installed. It was felt, however, that some change in the Shepheard plant was needed if full advantage of stainless steel was to be taken. Because of the use of vacuum and pressure the aluminium holding tanks had to be cylindrical and relatively thick. By making all transfers by pump at atmospheric pressure and controlling the flows to and from the holding vessels by stainless steel rotary valves, it became possible to combine the positive holding and security of the Shepheard plant with use of thin rectangular stainless steel holding tanks that gave notable savings in both space and cost as well as the ability to handle greater throughputs.

The plant was termed the 'Synchro' because of the synchronised controlled timing of the valves involved. It was put on the market in 1938 and a number were sold with throughputs up to 3,000 gallons per hour (Illustration 11). It was not really a success. In a year or two the holder system was to be replaced in the United Kingdom by the HTST process, so perhaps it never had a chance.

The need for a smaller and cheaper plate had been apparent for some time. It was also realised that improved heat transfer could be achieved if the plate spacing were reduced. Goodman worked out a pressed plate in which the rubbers for both sides lay side by side in grooves running parallel round the plate and so occupied roughly half the thickness of two superimposed gaskets of the same dimensions. Thus the plate spacing could be halved without reducing the depth of the rubbers and so maintain the same elastic properties in them.

This meant doing away with the reinforcing frame used in the HS and HL. Seligman was loath to do this but, fortunately, York Ice in the United States, who were manufacturing a modification of the HS and HL under licence, had never used the frame. After examination of these plates over a year, it was accepted that it was superfluous. In the meantime, Williams had been completing a series of strip heat exchange tests to determine the final dimensions and by the end of 1938 the new small HT plate was ready for production. But now came further delay.

Ironically, it resulted from the patent position. Learning the lesson of the HER, the new machines and auxiliaries had been patented in every detail and in many overseas countries. The patent for the twin-rubbered plate was filed in England in the spring of 1936. In the autumn of that year, Bergedorfer Eisenwerke of Hamburg, a subsidiary of AB Separator of Stockholm (Alfa-Laval), had quite independently filed a patent in Germany showing a twin-rubbered plate. The corresponding foreign APV patents, twenty-five of them, were filed as usual in the spring of 1937 with priority under international convention from the date of the British application in 1936. Then an accident occurred with this. Owing to what was euphemistically termed a 'clerical error' it was not sent to the Patent Office for sealing by the proper date and so became void. Although the application was refiled, it did not now have precedence over Bergedorf's and, had that been acceptable, the Gilbertian situation would have been reached in which the company would have been debarred from manufacturing or selling in Britain though free to do so everywhere else.

However, it was maintained that Bergedorf's patent was insufficiently precise and, although they adopted all sorts of blocking action, this view was eventually supported by the British Patent Office. In the meantime, it had been decided at Wandsworth to proceed. The necessary press tools were prepared, a process requiring many months, and the first

78

experimental plate was pressed in June 1939, three weeks before the Patent Office made its pronouncement.

This freed the company to go ahead but it left a number of countries where APV could not forbid Bergedorf to market their Astra plates which were at the root of this complex dispute. They consisted of a channel type plate pressed in stainless steel with twin rubber grooves, not as efficient as the APV plates but a serious competitor.

Bergedorf, of course, adopted what delaying tactics they could and so APV had to take legal action for infringement in a number of countries. When the case came up in France, the first to be heard, it was disclosed that in 1934 Bergedorf had proposed in a German 'petty patent' the use of gaskets side by side on a sheet metal plate. In many countries such 'petty patents' have no invalidating effect but in France they have.

Seligman visited Alfa-Laval (they had ceased to be APV agents some time before) to try and reach some accommodation in March 1939 but in vain. Later that year, the case was found against APV in France but in favour in Holland where the same conditions held. Subsequently four further decisions in the company's favour were found in Denmark, Sweden, Austria and Germany, the last in spite of it being against an important German firm and after war had been declared.

Bergedorf withdrew their plate in a number of markets and substituted one that did not infringe the APV patents. So ended this extraordinary affair. It could have been of great importance to both companies but, as it was, it had no direct effect. The war saw to that. The only definite result was the souring of relations between Seligman and Alfa-Laval.

The technical success of the HT encouraged Seligman and Goodman to investigate the possibility of applying the same principle to a larger plate but they gave up the idea as impracticable. The experience gained on groove design and pressing technology, however, encouraged them to redesign the HL plate with a view to obtaining a higher rate of heat transmission, so making better use of expensive material.

The experimental work was carried out and the full scale plate and production tools were designed, so work was well advanced when war broke out and the project had to be halted.

While the new stainless steel machines were dominating the dairy market, sales of the old gunmetal HER machine were still continuing. Even in the dairy it had been extraordinarily successful. By 1936, 864 machines had been installed, over 60% abroad. Of this total 250 were delivered between June 1933 and September 1936; 73% of them for export. Export markets included twenty-one countries of which Germany was the largest although almost static since 1932. Next was the United States where the market had expanded rapidly over the period 1933 to 1936 during which they accounted for nearly 30% of the total sales. Then followed Canada, Holland, Sweden and New Zealand. It was doubtless no coincidence that sales were best where the company had licensed local manufacture. At this juncture the deliveries to France were poor and to Australia negligible. The number of machines in Italy was not large but important; it included the central dairies for Milan and Rome. By no means all were for city milk, however. Machines in Holland and New Zealand, for example, were largely for cheese milk.

Outside the milk industry, the HER remained the dominant machine, particularly in the breweries who, conservative as ever, were much slower in adopting stainless steel machines than were the dairy firms.

Modified HER plates with channels double the normal width and half the depth were put into production so that the rate of cooling over a critical temperature range required for some brewery applications, could be controlled within wide limits. Subsequently plates with shallow channels of the normal width, and later still plates with channels of double width, were produced. A compound of these new plates with the original ones also enabled much greater flexibility and accuracy in designing machines for a particular duty.

By January 1940, 330 HER machines were at work in breweries, two-thirds of them for wort cooling and only one-sixth of them abroad, a wholly different position to the dairy markets. Australia and New Zealand accounted for over 50% of these exports.

The HER found a very big variety of other applications. Far the most important were in the alcohol and beet sugar industries especially in distilleries – whether for whisky or industrial alcohol – yeast plants and beet extraction units. For these and other chemical applications, rather more than 200 machines were at work at the beginning of 1940, a third of them abroad. France, whose beet sugar and industrial alcohol industries were predominant at this time – their petrol had to contain a substantial proportion of alcohol by law – was the best overseas market, accounting for over half the exports for all chemical duties.

Thus the sales pattern for heat exchangers was widely different for the chemical as compared with the dairy or brewery industries. Partly this was due to the much higher technical demands on salesmen to these industries, demands that agents, however skilled in dairy matters, were not trained to meet. Nor, naturally, did they know their potential customers. Thus the selling devolved in the main on the staff at Wandsworth.

The technical staff in what had now become the Chemical Engineering Department (CED), consisted of Ralph, W. H. A. ('Bill') Webb, a young graduate chemical engineer of great technical ability, who joined the firm in 1933, and R. R. ('Reggie') Webster who made up what he lacked in academic qualifications by good Scottish common sense, an inexhaustible capacity for work and a most winning disposition. Webster was the man of all work when he was not dealing with varnish plants and the whisky distilleries of Scotland.

Ralph, and then Webb, splendidly backed by the drawing office and works, did extremely well in the chemical industry not just in selling HER machines on their own but in distillation plant with which the heat exchangers were linked for the most part. After a number of them had been sold to Courtaulds, British Industrial Solvents (part of DCL) and others, one of them caught the eye of some French technicians. As a result an APV heat exchanger was sold to the Usines de Melle, who held the patents for a number of distillation processes including the best at that time for the production of absolute (water-free) alcohol for motor fuel by azeotropic distillation. This led to an association although to no formal agreement for their processes. Melle, however, undertook to recommend the use of APV heat exchangers in their installations.

In the meantime, an order for a large plant to produce high-grade alcohol from molasses was laid by Solvent Products of Dagenham. This was the first major alcohol plant to be totally designed by APV. It went to work in 1935 and performed excellently. With this job the Chemical Engineering Department came of age.

A year or two earlier, the company had been offered the rights to a new type of distillation plate patented by J. H. West, a DCL engineer. As patented, it looked a dreadful bag of tricks but Ralph saw that it combined the advantages of the bubble-cap and perforated types, then commonly in use. A prototype was produced and successfully tested and it was decided to take it further.

It was obvious that a lot of fundamental investigation and development would be needed. This would entail carrying out distillation work with highly inflammable materials and, if alcohol was involved, under excise restrictions. There was nowhere on the Wandsworth site remotely suitable, nor was there anyone equipped to carry out the work except Webb and he could not be spared.

After much consideration, the Board decided in 1935 to set up a special research laboratory for the purpose. It would cost, it was thought, £2,000 to £3,000 and at least £1,000 a year to run but it was believed that this could readily be recouped by the new business that would be brought in. Building was started in May and completed by the end of the year. It consisted of a spacious still house capable of accommodating columns up to forty feet in height with a laboratory for analysis attached, both of them arranged to be fire-proof. It must have been one of the best designed and equipped laboratories of its kind in the country.

A young graduate physical chemist, G. A. ('Tony') Dummett, was engaged to pursue research in the new laboratory. He had had several years' experience on a big coke-oven plant in South Yorkshire.

Work started in October in the test house next door to the still house which was not yet finished. It led to important results confirming work done by Professor Emil Kirschbaum in Karlsruhe on the effect of direction of flow of liquid over distillation plants. It was applied in the design of the new plates.

Subsequently, in the still house, a long series of experiments gradually exposed the mechanism of operation, the capacity and efficiency, under limited conditions, of the West plate. Progress was of necessity very slow and after two years had passed, the Board was beginning to get restive for results, especially as no large orders had accrued.

By the end of 1937, however, the position had so far progressed that it was possible to calculate what the probable performance of a West column would be and a sensible redesign of the plate had been patented. At this point, DCL at Hull required a still to reprocess all the reject streams from the distillery there, a quite horrible duty. A West column was offered and accepted. It did a first-rate job. The efficiency of the West plate had been abundantly proved.

In the meantime DCL had decided to install a major 800 gallon per hour Melle absolute fuel alcohol plant at their Hammersmith distillery, the largest such unit in the world at that time. The job was given to APV to manufacture from drawings made by Barbet, Melle's French licencees. Serious faults were found both in the drawings and in the plant after it went to work in 1938 but the plant was modified by APV and thereafter worked admirably.

APV at this juncture were probably leaders, in Europe at least, in alcohol and solvent plant design. War and the development of the petrochemical industries prevented the company reaping its full reward.

The first immediate fruit was an order for a large Melle fuel alcohol plant in Australia in 1939. This was manufactured at Wandsworth and shipped to the Antipodes where it went to work without a hitch.

Distillation was not the only unit operation investigated in the new still house. In early 1937, the company took an option on a patent by Kirschbaum on the improvement of the performance of natural circulation evaporators. A full scale experimental unit was built and experiments started. In no way could Kirschbaum's results be reproduced except under operating conditions that would never be needed in practice.

The evaporator experiments were not wasted, however. A great deal had been learnt about the operation of natural circulation tubular evaporators under various conditions, enough to permit design of commercial units.

During 1938 and 1939 several substantial evaporators were installed, all based on the still house experiments, but once more the war stopped further development just as it seemed that the company was evolving an important new product.

In the dairy industry, experiments were started on a process that was to become increasingly important, cream pasteurising and degassing prior to butter making. In 1934 a simple vacuum degasser was patented. This was found to remove volatile taints as well. Early in 1936 it could be claimed that it was in successful use in all the principal dairying and butter-making countries in the world.

The degasser found other applications, to milk naturally but more importantly to fruit juices. Seligman had for some time believed, rightly, that there would be major expansion in the market for fresh fruit juices and that APV could play a useful part in it. The first development was that of an HTST pasteurising and degassing plant at the Agricultural and Horticultural Research Station at Long Ashton. Apple, pineapple and grapefruit were treated very successfully, lemon and orange less so.

Work on these and other processes in the UK, and also some started in Spain and Switzerland, was halted by the war.

Another side of the business got an immense fillip in 1934 when the Finance Act greatly increased the tax on unladen weight of transport vehicles and also gave a vehicle with an unladen weight of less than 2½ tons the advantage of an extra 10 mph over the legal limit of 20 mph imposed on heavier vehicles. The reduced weight of aluminium tanks therefore gave the possibility of increased capacity at the same load, reduced tax or increased number of journeys per day.

The company took full advantage of this situation. Tanks were redesigned and a number of patents taken out. Sales increased greatly, mostly for petrol. Stainless steel tankers were also developed for milk and beer to support the range of aluminium tanks that had been marketed since 1912.

It was rightly thought that design in this rapidly expanding field should be in the hands of a man with more experience of it. Accordingly, a transport tank section was set up with S. G. Betts as leader. He resembled nothing so much as a benevolent Sergeant-Major (which in fact he had been during the war) and had seen service in the transport tank department of an oil company.

About 1935, a change began to take place in the varnish trade. Up until then the business had been mainly with hundreds of little firms who carried on the whole gamut of gum running, stand oil manufacture and preparation of special finishes in a single small shop. From this time demand developed for units of much larger and more complicated design. In 1938 the company began to get into this heavier class of plant.

The remarkable increase in dairy business called for an extension of staff. Menzies was doing a magnificent job. Over the years 1933 to 1938, the sales credited to him in the UK averaged 20% of the total turnover of the company, including export. Nevertheless, he and Wyatt could not do everything and another man was needed, better qualified academically than the others.

The choice fell on Jack Matthews, a graduate chemist, who had spent some years selling for the Power Petroleum Company. It proved an inspired choice. He joined the company in February 1933 and was sent straight to the Dairy Show at Olympia to be greeted by Seligman with, 'I hope you will be happy in your new surroundings but, nevertheless, feel sure you will not.' He was mainly concerned with the more difficult technical jobs particularly for the Milk Marketing Board who were equipping a number of new creameries at this time. He was therefore involved in a number of new developments, the pasteurisation of cheese milk and later condensed and powdered milk and butter. He proved a brilliant salesman, as reliable in the office as on the road, and was destined for a distinguished career in the company.

The number of plants in operation now demanded a lot of service. Accordingly, J. R. ('Reg') Cuttell, who had joined the company as a draughtsman in 1928, was appointed a service engineer in 1934. So started a career of great value to the company for he was possessed of technical imagination of a high order.

The overseas business of the company expanded to an even greater extent than the home. In 1937 it reached nearly 25% of the total.

The most striking developments were in North America. York continued to sell well in the United States. With the advent of stainless steel, they had designed and were marketing a modified form of the HER made from two stainless sheet pressings welded together. The company had expected York to market the new HL and HS for which the Board was prepared to grant a new licence. York, however, maintained that the new plates were no more than an 'improvement' on the old and so covered by the existing agreement at a considerably lower royalty. The situation was becoming very confused when Seligman revealed that he had not assigned the rights of his basic United States patent to the company, nor would he do so until either a proper return was assured or an English court ruled that the new design constituted no more than an 'improvement' legally. Within a month, York had climbed down, a new agreement was sealed in August 1935 and they set up production of the new plates.

They decided to concentrate on the dairy industry where they did extremely well and, towards the end of 1935, abrogated their rights to the brewery business. Thus APV was left without means of marketing to the non-dairy industries in the vast United States market.

In mid-1938, Wilson returned from a visit to North America and reported that Wallace had suggested setting up a joint selling company in which APV should take a half share financially. The Board regarded the idea favourably and in the autumn agreed to invest in the project.

So, at the beginning of 1939, Walker-Wallace Incorporated, the first APV overseas subsidiary company, was established in Buffalo, New York State, with Wallace as President and Seligman and Wilson Directors. To everyone's satisfaction it operated straight away without loss.

Earlier, a new ten-year agreement had been reached with the parent company in Toronto. Apart from the usual dairy and brewery lines the two Walker-Wallace companies were particularly successful in introducing APV to the wine and fruit juice industries.

In Germany, by mid-1934, the company had been involved for a whole two years in disputes and law suits with Holstein und Kappert with the result that sales, which had been extremely good initially, had reduced to a mere trickle. A new agreement was negotiated but, by then, Hitler was well in the saddle and very little business resulted. At the outbreak of war there does not seem to have been a single APV machine operating in German breweries.

In Scandinavia, the agency of Alfa-Laval was superseded and in August 1938, Claesson and Petersen, who for some years had been getting exceptionally good sales in Sweden, were appointed agents for dairies in the Scandinavian countries and the then independent Baltic States. The principal was Waleur Petersen, no technologist but a first rate salesman to the dairy industry. Within a year, however, he was proposing to sell his business to the Swedish Farmers' Association and the company was faced with the problem of protecting what had become a very important sector of the export market. Then at the outbreak of war, Petersen announced his intention to go into liquidation; he feared the growing Danish competition. The Board considered taking over the business themselves but no agreement could be arrived at and in the end Petersen sold out to Wedholm's in Stockholm. So ended a chapter; APV never regained their dominance of the Scandinavian market.

In Australia, sales of the company's products were at last developing, particularly in breweries. In the dairy industry, too, things were looking up. Although the first APV heat exchanger was delivered in 1929, it was not until 1935 that the first city milk plant was sold. This was in Sydney. Thereafter the volume of business rapidly increased.

A draughtsman from Wandsworth was sent to give assistance to Bryant's. This was the first of a series of exports of technical personnel from the centre to subsidiary companies and associates that has formed an essential part of APV overseas policy ever since.

In Europe, political unrest was beginning to have a serious effect on business. The bloody Civil War totally disrupted the Spanish dairy industry and in Austria, where Norbert Ullman was active and got a number of useful orders, all activity was cut off by Hitler's invasion in 1938.

In France, even though a decree making pasteurisation mandatory was propagated in 1939, nothing could happen before the war so it was only much later that the company could develop this market.

Another country closed to APV by political pressures, though of quite a different kind, was Ireland who steadily refused to buy from England. The HER could only be sold by having it manufactured in Denmark and sold by Silkeborg. Ironically, it was only the outbreak of war, in which Ireland remained neutral, that altered the situation.

One other agency was important, not for any large business it brought in but for the implications for the future. Thomas had visited South America and reported that the only long-term prospects were in Brazil. History has proved him right but at that time the only result was the appointment of Oscar Landmann in Sao Paulo as agent, a first small step towards the eventual APV do Brasil.

The further heavy expansion in the company's turnover and in the type of manufacture led to increasing demands for space. Even in 1934, output was only being met by night shifts and overtime in spite of the extensions made only a year or two before.

No immediate action was taken but a year later the Board authorised an extension to the metal working shop. No special arrangements to finance this were considered necessary.

The only extra space available for a major extension of the works was occupied by the line of picturesque but unsanitary cottages lining Point Pleasant. These were condemned by the Borough Council at the beginning of 1936, thus freeing the hands of the company who now owned them. In May 1938, a new extension to the works on the site of the cottages and a completely new office block to replace the temporary hut alongside Northfields House were authorised. At the same time an enlargement of the existing foundry was agreed.

Included in this was much new plant. Power presses for the new plates and more precise machines for jig and tool production had become essential parts of APV manufacture.

The extensions were finished early in 1939. The new shop was used for assembly of transport tanks at one end and of heat exchangers at the other. The office block accommodated a drawing office, design and dairy engineering departments, and accounts and records. Directors, chemical and brewery engineers remained in Northfields. This was the last major building project on the Wandsworth site.

With all the increased activity the turnover and profits rose sharply. From some £331,000 in 1934, turnover increased to £532,000 in 1939 while profits rose from £36,700 to £68,800 accordingly. Dividends totalling 25% free of income tax were paid each year. These results were achieved even though the whole cost of the experimental work to produce the new heat exchangers was written off against revenue.

The fair value of the shares rose steadily from £2 10s in 1934 to £4 in 1939 as a result.

There was also some indication of increased efficiency of operation. The total number of employees did not increase substantially – from 740 in 1934 to 780 in 1939. At the same time the ratio of turnover to productive wages rose from 5.3 to 6.3 (for comparison the figure was 5.9 in 1914; 5.1 in 1921 and 5.3 in 1929).

Nevertheless, in spite of such rosy appearances, the Board was not free of financial care. Basically it hinged on cash flow. Up to 1935, the company had managed to meet the costs of expansion, whether of buildings or technical development, from revenue with little or no recourse to bank overdraft. From then on the requirements for capital expenditure and for working capital to finance the greater turnover could no longer be met from revenue. Bank overdraft rose to £22,000 in 1936 and remained at about that level until 1939 when in addition a bank capital loan of £34,000 was established.

In 1938, Wilson reviewed the cash position for the Board. A measure of his problem is shown by the increase in value of fixed assets from £75,000 in 1933 to £120,000 in 1939; at the same time the value of work in progress had more than doubled. He reckoned that it would be quite justifiable to use bank overdraft for working capital but not to finance further fixed assets.

He pointed out that the alternatives were clear. Capital expenditure would be needed if the level of profits was to be maintained. This could only come from profits or new capital. The dividend was equivalent to 10% on paid up capital plus profits accumulated in the business. He preferred to leave the money in the business where it was needed rather than pay increased dividends. This sensible view prevailed.

All the same, it was clear that the firm was short of capital. In June 1938, Seligman Brothers offered, and the Board accepted, credit facilities to finance purchase of raw materials and sales. On two occasions, early in 1936 and at the end of 1939, the possibility of floating APV as a public company was discussed but rejected.

Additions were made to the Board. Some technical stiffening was looked for, so in January 1938 they elected Geoffrey Blackman, Seligman's son-in-law, then with ICI but later to become Professor of Agricultural Economy at Oxford and Vice-President of the Royal Society. In his quiet way he was to contribute a lot to the company.

At the beginning of 1936, Seligman's second son Peter joined the company and so started a distinguished career. He was a Cambridge graduate in engineering and afterwards he had had a year or so of industrial experience. As early as 1933 Wilson had sent Seligman a memorandum on Peter's introduction to the company. In it he had recommended that Peter should not be given prolonged outside experience before joining the firm and, rather against his better judgement though doubtless following his paternal inclination, Seligman agreed.

He was put to work on the commercial side mainly under Wilson's direction. Wilson, always an autocratic character and now becoming increasingly so, no doubt resented Peter's introduction to the company even if he did not admit it to himself. However, at the beginning of 1939 Peter was formally elected to the Board.`

Wilson, himself, was outwardly prospering in the company. His agreement was renewed for five years from 1935, his emoluments were increased and he was allowed to take up 4,000 new shares.

Behind the scenes, however, relations between him and Seligman were steadily worsening. In 1936 a report from Whitlock on works reorganisation led to further recriminations. There had been trouble over deliveries, particularly of transport tanks. Whitlock analysed the position and the existing organisation, laid a good deal of the blame on the sales departments and the drawing office and recommended an increase in works staff, machines and eventually space to solve the problem. It was a persuasive document, critical by implication of Wilson, and ended by suggesting that dual control of the drawing office and works should cease.

In principle it was accepted. Wilson always resented it and relations between the sales and works organisation deteriorated.

In the spring of 1939, relations between the two Managing Directors had become so strained that Seligman wrote to Wilson blaming him for 'the bitterness that surrounded the place', for his expressions of dissatisfaction especially as to the works and for failing to seek the root causes of the difficulties. Wilson, naturally enough, disagreed and appealed to personal friendship.

Later in the year, Seligman proposed a re-allotment of responsibilities in which Peter, now regarded by Seligman as 'one of the three in daily direction of the company' would take charge of production including both works and drawing office. Wilson flatly disagreed. He thought that no change was called for in an organisation that had worked well and that Peter should remain as assistant to the Managing Director.

Things were now getting so tense that Gerald Seligman intervened to smooth them over. By then both Seligman and Wilson were talking of Wilson leaving the company. Gerald believed that both had got too overwrought to look at things dispassionately. He himself had a good deal of sympathy with both sides. Whether it was this conciliatory action or the effect of the outbreak of war, the situation was patched up and Wilson's agreement was renewed for a further five years early in 1940. Moritz, had he lived, might have held the ring between the two but, as it was, too much bitterness had been brought to the surface for any accommodation to be more than temporary.

As it happened, 1935 saw the Silver Jubilee celebrations of the coronation of George V and the twenty-fifth anniversary of the founding of the company within a few weeks of each other. Jubilation was in the air. Hourly workers got a paid holiday and a special gift of £1 on 6 May, the date of the Royal Jubilee. In addition a garden party was given for the staff in the grounds of Lincoln House on 22 June.

Other more substantial benefits for employees were established. The staff bonus quadrupled during the period from 1934 to 1939. More important, a pension scheme was introduced. By autumn 1937 the staff benefit fund had reached a total that justified using it as a basis to provide pensions for workpeople and to establish a contributory staff pension scheme which was accordingly set up a year later.

Since the rise of the axis powers, Seligman, prompted at least as much by generous political principles as by racial sympathies, and his wife had been quietly active in giving aid to refugees from German and Italian aggression.

In 1936 when Haile Selassie, Emperor of Ethiopia, was driven from his kingdom by Mussolini's forces, he took refuge in Britain where he was Seligman's guest at Lincoln House, and a number of Germans and Austrians were given posts on the company's staff, both at home and abroad, where several gave distinguished service.

From 1938, the company, like the country, was overshadowed by the threat of war. Early in 1939 a series of underground air-raid shelters were being built on the waste ground between the offices and Point Pleasant, looking for all the world like a series of neolithic barrows. These could take 300 people while others were distributed in and around the main works building.

These shelters were not a precautionary measure provided by a benevolent employer but, since the invasion of Czechoslovakia by

Hitler in March of that year, had been made compulsory by Act of Parliament. They were much disliked by those who were supposed to use them and were ignored by many people.

Now, too, began several developments prompted by expected war-time needs. In many countries the HTST (high temperature, short time) process was accepted for milk pasteurisation and APV had supplied many plants to operate it. It did not require so much corrosion resistant material in its manufacture as did holder processes and so there was likely to be pressure to use it in Britain during war time. At the same time work on continuous holders was accelerated and led to the design and manufacture of 'retarder' plates to fit in the plate pack of a heat exchanger and so provide the necessary holding time within a single frame.

The Chemical Engineering Department was already handling direct war work. A number of copper distillation units and heat exchangers were designed and sold for acetone recovery in the cordite section of the great Royal Ordnance factories that were being built mostly in western Scotland. TNT melting plants and other equipment in aluminium were also being supplied.

The most far-reaching development came in toluole plants. First, Newton Chambers, Dummett's old employer in south Yorkshire, approached APV and asked the company to design some batch distillation units for producing highly refined toluene for TNT manufacture from the benzole produced on coke-oven plants. They were designed purely on work done in the new laboratory and all met their guarantees, which were stringent.

Almost simultaneously, the company was approached by the Appleby-Frodingham Steel Company at Scunthorpe, a subsidiary of the United Steel Companies, to install a continuous distillation unit to produce pure benzene and toluene from the crude benzole from their coke-oven plants. The plant was calculated on first principles and gained the order for the first continuous benzole products distillation plant in Britain.

All such plants had to be manufactured from cast iron and mild steel. This represented a completely new departure for APV in which CED acted as main contractor, designing, procuring, erecting and commissioning the whole plant but manufacturing practically none of it. Seligman and Wilson had some doubts of the commercial viability of these contracts for none of the efforts of the engineers would bring any work to the shops nor bear their full share of overheads. Nevertheless, it was decided to go ahead as a contribution to the war effort. So started a side of the company's business that was to be of considerable importance over the next twenty years.

Ralph saw the possibilities of other work in the coke-oven industry. Very soon there were orders for further toluene plants including an even bigger continuous pure-products plant from another United Steel's factory, the coke-oven and tar refinery at Orgreave, near Sheffield.

And so, far better equipped to meet the demands on it than it had been twenty-five years before, the company entered a second period of war that was bound to interrupt its development with unpredictable consequences.

# Chapter 7
# The Second World War
## 1939–1945

'Armament questions and the possibilities of war have overshadowed business generally: consequently when the actual outbreak took place on 3 September, it was accompanied by a curious sense of relief. The extent and duration of the calamity no man can say. It is being entered upon with an absence of enthusiasm or excitement, but with a cold calm which, if directed and maintained, will see us through a long and difficult period. It is just a necessary and difficult job thrust upon us which we have to see through.'

The opening words of the editorial to the September 1939 number of the APV *Quarterly Technical Bulletin*, an excellent little journal for circulation to APV agents and staff, reflected very well the attitude of most people in the company to the declaration of war with Germany. Unlike 1914, it had been long expected and was greeted with none of the euphoria that the first war had engendered. Rather the reverse, for many realised that the country was ill prepared for the conflict and anticipated cataclysmic ruin from enemy bombing.

Unexpectedly, the first months went by with singularly little change to everyday life beyond the effects of all sorts of Government controls: rationing, the black-out, the evacuation of children from the great cities, and import controls, among them.

The company had already embarked on a number of the lines of production of war material it was to pursue during the war and these were accentuated. The Government was faced with difficulties of foreign currency for imports if exports were not maintained. It therefore became an essential part of war-time business to maintain overseas trade as far as possible. Moreover, the milk industry formed an essential sector of the carefully balanced scheme of food rationing so that even at home the dairy business suffered much less than might have been expected. In the first few months there was a considerable backlog of orders to be dealt with and later developments during the war ensured a reasonable amount of dairy work for which scarce raw materials could be allocated.

Chemical engineering, transport tanks and sheet metal fabrication were all clearly going to have to be used directly in the war effort. It was for the most part the brewery and varnish businesses that were going to suffer.

In effect, the problems facing the company were less of development or marketing – it was well equipped to meet these – than those of organisation and finance, especially in the long term.

At the outbreak of war, Wilson reviewed the likely effects to the Board. There would be delays in export business and direct Government contracts would not be done against progress payments. There would therefore be limitations of cash flow and the overdraft would increase. In this he was perfectly correct. He went on to estimate a turnover of £400,000 per annum under war conditions which was grossly pessimistic.

Even so, he did not anticipate much change in staff. Most of the workforce and staff were in 'reserved' occupations and would have had difficulty in getting accepted in the Forces in any case.

As in 1914, however, a number of mostly more junior people joined up. Among those who enlisted was a junior laboratory assistant, W. S. ('Robby') Robinson, who, after service as a Blenheim pilot and with the Chindits in Burma, eventually became Managing Director of APV do Brasil.

Things moved along more or less smoothly with the company, like the country as a whole, rather slowly getting into its war-time stride until, in May 1940, the German attack that was to lead to Dunkirk and the fall of France broke out; Churchill became Prime Minister and the nation was suddenly plunged into urgent activity.

As far as APV was concerned this was, in the main, involved with starting up the acetone and toluene distillation plants that were just coming on stream. The most important of these was the new and in many ways novel continuous benzole plant at Appleby-Frodingham in Scunthorpe. Initially it was not functioning properly, not as it turned out because of any basic failure of design. Eventually, some relatively simple modifications were worked out and installed. In a short time the plant had exceeded its guarantees on all counts.

Thus success was achieved out of what had looked, at the start, like failure. The modifications were used on the larger continuous plant at Orgreave near Sheffield so that that started up without trouble a year or so later. Appleby-Frodingham also installed a repeat plant of larger throughput some years later.

The summer of 1940 was a brilliant one with almost continuous sun and clear skies so that it was no surprise when, in late August, the Luftwaffe launched its attack on Britain. At first this was aimed at the Air Force but when the Battle of Britain had been won by the RAF, the German tactics changed to bombing attacks on London.

To begin with these were in daylight. One lovely morning in early September, APV staff on their way to work stopped and watched an extraordinary air battle between RAF Spitfires and Hurricanes and squadrons of German bombers in faultless formation with their flocks of attendant fighters, being fought over their heads. No one seemed to worry about falling bombs. A few fell in the area about this time but no great damage was done. Soon all this was to change.

Shortly afterwards the real Blitz began. For fifty-seven nights on end, London was under air attack and, although the western suburbs suffered less than the eastern or the centre, the damage was still severe and the strain, on some at least, great. Most people, however, found unsuspected reserves of endurance and humour that saw them through. The daily retailing of ghoulish horror stories in the office became the subject of small fines gladly paid and given to war charity.

Fortunately APV survived this period with no more than slight damage although there was much trouble due to water, gas or telephones being cut off by bomb damage elsewhere. Betts had been made joint Air Raid Precautions Controller with responsibility for the offices. According to his diaries, there were periods of 'alert' for ARP personnel amounting to an average of ten hours out of every twenty-four during the whole three months of September, October and November, but as this was mostly after dark, actual productive hours did not suffer as badly as might have been expected.

For many of the staff, this period was a baptism of fire. Even before the outbreak of war, some had enlisted in the ARP, Fire and Ambulance Services; many more joined later on. When France capitulated and the threat of invasion became acute, the Home Guard was established and APV recruited a platoon.

During the Blitz, the Home Guard mounted all-night guards from 2 September on; fire watchers dealt with incendiary bombs, several of which fell through roofs causing minor fires; the ARP personnel manned their various services; and the spotters from their post on the roof watched the course of the raids and kept the rest informed of any incident as it arose.

At about the turn of the year the night raids that had already largely been shifted to other targets than London started to decrease in intensity. From then until mid-1944 when the 'Doodle-bug' raids started, Wandsworth was relatively free from air attack and life returned to something approaching normal.

While all this was going on, the company had steadily been developing its war potential. As in the first war, one of its most important products was tanks for aircraft. These were now of much more sophisticated design, in shape, in strength and in material. They had to be fabricated with a high degree of accuracy and in

99

large numbers, so that series production with specialised jigs and tooling was essential. Above all, sufficient skilled labour was not available so, as in the first war, women were trained, particularly as welders, and excellent craftspeople they proved.

There was no space available at Point Pleasant, so in mid-1940 a shop was rented in Kimber Road not far away in Wandsworth. Towards the end of 1942 an order was laid by the Ministry of Aircraft Production for petrol tanks for Vickers Spitfires, the most successful British fighter plane, to be made in magnesium elektron, the least dense of common alloys. The Kimber Road factory had to be specially laid out and a lot of preliminary development work done on pressing the complex shapes as well as on welding a material quite unfamiliar to APV.

By mid-1943, the aircraft tank business had grown so far that Kimber Road was let off and new premises rented in Garratt Lane, Wandsworth, close by, and laid out fully equipped for line production.

The manufacture of elektron tanks was difficult and time consuming. Alternative methods of tank production were accordingly put under investigation at Point Pleasant. The design work fell mainly to Goodman and the welding and metallurgical work to W. K. B. ('Bill') Marshall who had replaced Hignett as Chief Metallurgist when he left to join International Nickel as their welding specialist in 1940.

The problem was to produce a tank of identical dimensions, strength and corrosion resistance with a substantial reduction in production hours. The solution was brilliantly imaginative and successful. The alloy of aluminium with 3% magnesium is substantially stronger and more rigid than pure aluminium or, even, magnesium elektron. The tank could accordingly be made in thinner material but there were considerable problems of design, spot-welding and production engineering to be worked out. In the end, the company finished up with one of the finest production lines in the country for producing welded tanks in these difficult materials and the aluminium alloy tank was made in one-third the production hours required for those in elektron with even a slight reduction in weight.

In all nearly 3,500 of these Spitfire tanks were made and there was a good deal of repair work, too. But this did not end the aircraft tank work. Towards the end of the war, the most successful British fighter-bomber was the Mosquito. For this nearly 2,500 fuel tanks in aluminium alloy were manufactured at Garratt Lane.

Transport tanks were needed on a huge scale both for desert warfare and for the invasion of Europe. They were of simple standard design but made of mild steel, not aluminium or stainless steel, the materials to which the APV workforce was accustomed. A special shop was acquired and equipped for this more rudimentary work and some 3,000 were fabricated.

Even before the war much of the foundry output was given over to Alpax castings for the Navy. This work continued but the long-standing relations with the Admiralty led to APV undertaking a lot of highly secret development work, including radar. E. L. ('Len') Smith, a young foundry salesman, was responsible for the company's dealings with the Admiralty. His career in the company was to be meteoric, if short.

Apart from the coke-oven toluene and acetone plants, the Chemical Engineering Department dealt with a number of other distillation plants and development continued in the distillation laboratory throughout the war. In addition to process development the work on the West plate was extended.

Early in the war, Ralph had approached the Ministry of Supply and offered to apply APV's research facilities to any distillation problem that concerned them. They posed that of 'low gravity' toluene. The toluene in gas-works benzole, of which there was a considerable amount at that time, for all town gas was then derived from the carbonisation of coal, is contaminated with other relatively low density hydrocarbons from which it cannot be separated by simple distillation. In the production of TNT, these interfere with the nitration process, reduce the yield and lower the quality of explosive. The problem was how to produce pure toluene, free from these extraneous components, by distillation from gas-works crude.

Extended tests in the distillation laboratory led to a completely novel process that was patented. A batch unit was shown to work in the laboratory with a large variety of crudes but no interest seemed to be shown in it until, quite suddenly, in 1942 the Ministry of Supply ordered a plant to deal with the whole of the gas-works crudes of Scotland at the Provanmill tar refinery of the City of Glasgow's Gas Department.

The batch process was redesigned to operate on a continuous basis following a series of still house trials and the plant, now being erected at Provanmill, was altered to operate the new continuous 'pseudo-azeotropic' process. It was started up in the summer of 1943, operated virtually without a hitch and not only met all its guarantees but produced the best nitration toluene in the country regardless of source.

In the meantime, considerable developments were taking place in the dairy industry. The designation of the 'high temperature, short time' (HTST) treatment of milk as 'pasteurisation' was legalised in 1941 and at a stroke revolutionised the industry.[1] One of the reasons for this was to economise on scarce raw materials; the complete process could be carried through in a single heat exchanger and the bulky holding tanks were eliminated. In a number of dairies the system had already been introduced *sub rosa*. Large numbers of school children were evacuated from the big cities which, though it reduced consumption somewhat in the large conurbations, caused large increases in the reception areas in some of which modern pasteurisation and distribution systems did not obtain.

As there was no legal objection to the HTST process unless the milk were to be sold designated as 'pasteurised', it offered a quick

[1] The final authorisation was signed at Seligman's desk in his Wimbledon home. As an acknowledged authority on pasteurisation, he had been active with the authorities in getting the necessary legal documents drafted.

solution to the rural dairyman's problems. Even in the city centres, a much more compact plant with easier cleaning, more rapid processing and smaller space requirements was attractive under war-time conditions. The only major objection earlier had been that it adversely affected cream line as compared with the holder process but, using the new stainless steel plates with hot water heating and at the conditions selected (162°F held for fifteen seconds minimum) this was shown to be a myth.

Much new business resulted immediately. APV with its long experience was well prepared to meet it.

Three essential new items of plant had had to be developed, however: a holding section in the heat exchanger of adequate efficiency to provide the necessary holding time accurately and consistently; temperature controllers of sufficient sensitivity to react virtually immediately if the temperature of milk entering the holder fell even minimally below the set level; and a flow diversion valve at the holder outlet, actuated by the temperature controller, that would divert the milk back to the inlet immediately if the pasteurisation temperature fell below the control value.

All these had been developed and tested before the new regulations came into force. They were not as sophisticated or accurate as they later became, but they were quite adequate to meet the immediate requirements so the new plants could be sold and put into service with complete confidence.

Thus, at a stroke, the days of the holder plant were ended. Since then, none have been sold. There were those at APV that believed this would lead to a serious fall in business. But the possibilities of new developments in milk processing that followed the universal adoption of HTST were enormous, though then hardly apparent, and entirely obliterated any loss there might have been. As Seligman said at the time, 'The better is often the enemy of the good,' and it is foolish to oppose it.

Even as it was, the production of dairy plant at APV remained at least at the pre-war level in real terms. In 1943, the output was at the rate of some £450,000 per annum equivalent to nearly half the total tunover of the company that year, including all the direct war work.

Problems arose in the dairy sales department. In November 1940, Wyatt's agreement was suddenly terminated and Matthews appointed Manager of the Dairy Engineering Department in his place. It proved an excellent appointment for, in a few years, Matthews had gained world-wide eminence as a dairy engineer as well as a salesman of APV plant.

Work at Wandsworth ran on a reasonably level keel once the bombing Blitz of 1940–41 was past. So it continued until, in June 1944, the Anglo-American invasion of France was launched, followed very shortly afterwards by the intensive bombing of London by the V1 flying bombs, popularly termed 'Doodle-bugs'. These were simple, ram-jet propelled, unmanned aircraft with a body filled with explosive. For many people they were less disturbing than manned bombers because they were more predictable but others, who had a deeper fear of inanimate machines than of mortal men, found them very frightening. Worst of all, they arrived in an uninterrupted stream, night and day. There was a perpetual air raid alert for several weeks on end, so that the ARP personnel were on practically continuous duty when they were not at work.

This bombardment had a considerable effect on the company. On 11 July, Baigent reported to the Board that over the previous three weeks 4,000 productive hours equivalent to one-sixth of total production had been lost in sheltering during alerts. Many of the women employed in the aircraft tank shop in Garratt Lane had left London and then on 6 July the shop itself had received a direct hit that would keep it and the rest of the Garratt Lane sites out of production for a week or two. In the office, some senior secretarial and other staff had left London, others had had severe damage to their homes that necessitated absence from duty and time was being lost during alerts. He pointed out that the financial consequences would be grave.

So things continued until the collapse of German resistance in

Normandy allowed the allied armies to sweep round to Calais and, by the beginning of September, the Doodle-bugs were finished.

By now the war work was virtually over and more and more attention was being devoted to the problems of the peace that was now clearly in prospect.

Insofar as it was possible, export business was encouraged and there were important developments in spite of the exigencies of war. One unexpected result was the opening up of a market in Ireland, previously virtually closed to the United Kingdom. In early 1940, arrangements were made for the Dairy Supply Co. Ltd (Desco), a subsidiary of United Dairies, to represent the company in both Eire and Northern Ireland.

In the United States, both York and Walker-Wallace Inc. operated successfully. At the beginning of 1940, York had sold over 100 HER and over 200 HS and HL machines. In mid-1942, the rate of royalty was revised. Walker-Wallace not only operated profitably on its own account but was able to feed a lot of work to York. Thus APV's position in America was maintained through the war, an important matter as the European markets had been almost wholly cut off.

At the outbreak of war, the company had engaged H. J. ('Henry') Lawless as an overseas salesman for distillation plant. He was a Lancastrian who had been employed by Barbet, had sold their alcohol plant in India and was entirely at home in France. In 1941, he visited Brazil and later India, and played an important part in developments there. In mid-1945 he visited France and eventually went to Paris to set up an office there that in the course of time became another APV subsidiary with himself as Chairman.

For some time it had been thought that India would offer a major market for alcohol plant based on the large indigenous sugar industry. A subsidiary company was contemplated and in this APV was given some general support by the authorities in Delhi. At the end of February 1944, Lawless was sent out to survey the position. He travelled by air, a rarity then. A few weeks later, he had opened

105

discussions with an Indian businessman on possible collaboration.

By the autumn it seemed that the negotiations had developed far enough to send out Bill Webb, as Managing Director-to-be of the new company, with Hugh Greenshields, then Production Engineer at Wandsworth, who was to plan the new factory. No sooner had they arrived than the Indian collaborator declared that he must be given complete control of the enterprise and accordingly, early in 1945, the partnership broke up.

Political feeling was running very high in these years just before independence. As a result, the attempts made by the company to continue the enterprise on its own, pending the inauguration of some new form of collaboration, were met with considerable opposition from Nationalist politicians. However, after protests that even reached the Cabinet in Whitehall, permission to proceed was granted, Lawless returned to Britain and by April the company was negotiating the lease of a site at Dum-Dum, near Calcutta.

In June, the APV Engineering Company was incorporated. A coppersmith inspector was despatched to look after the fabrication side of the undertaking. All seemed to be going well when the Indian Government laid down that 70% of the capital subscribed must be Indian. It took a further six months of wrangling and discussion, in Britain as well as India, until an arrangement was finally reached.

Thus, in somewhat stormy fashion, the first APV manufacturing subsidiary was established. With benefit of hindsight and from a purely commercial point of view, it was probably not a wise move. It locked up an unexpectedly large amount of capital that could ill be spared; it was to continue to pose problems that absorbed an excessive amount of management effort for years to come; and, for various reasons, India was to prove a disappointing market.

Not so, however, another developing country, Brazil. Again, it was the indigenous alcohol industry that provided the initial attraction though, as in India, that was not to be of decisive importance in the long term.

A joint manufacturing operation with Landmann & Filhos, the APV agents for dairy and brewery in Sao Paulo, was considered but eventually dropped. However, at that juncture, the dairy business in Sao Paulo changed completely. Prior to 1939, no modern pasteurising plant existed in the city; by the end of 1945 all five major supply companies had new APV plant and auxiliaries supplied by Landmann. This and developments in the brewery business were eventually to lead to that highly successful venture, APV do Brasil.

A similar development began to be considered in Australia. At the beginning of 1940, John Bryant was suggesting APV taking a share in his business which was to include setting up manufacturing facilities. While this was favourably regarded by the Board – it was in fact in accord with their general policy, agreed before the war – it was not until several years later that concrete proposals were before them.

Towards the end of 1945, Thomas travelled to Sweden, particularly to visit Wedholm's, the manufacturing company belonging to the Swedish Dairy Farmers' Co-operative to whom Petersen had sold his business and with it the APV agency. He reported unfavourably on the situation. Alfa-Laval had developed a competitive plate heat exchanger that might infringe APV patents and that was already under test by the official dairy authorities. He suspected that as a result Wedholm's were going to play for time over their agreement with the company. Thomas also contacted Petersen and arranged for him to represent APV in the dairy industries of Denmark, Finland and Norway.

By the end of 1945, European and Near-East markets were being opened up again, with France, Switzerland and Belgium under direction from Lawless in his Paris office.

War production had required a number of extra fabricating shops, Kimber Road, Garratt Lane and others. All were leased. There were two shops in Garratt Lane; one was the aircraft tank shop acquired on behalf of the Ministry of Aircraft Production. The other was used for more general APV work and, when the leases of the other shops were allowed to fall in at the end of the war, the freehold, not only of the shop occupied by the company but of the whole site of above an acre, was acquired. This was a wise move in view of how the business was to develop in the next few years.

At the outbreak of war when it was clear that a big increase in foundry output would be called for, it was decided to use the large shed already leased at Allsop's Wharf as an extension of the existing foundry. It was equipped with some second-hand machinery and new furnaces and went to work within a month. It was here, at the end of 1944, that the first APV stainless steel castings were made.

This was not the only addition to the company's permanent premises. The works staff had increased very substantially and the offices had become too small to house them all. Towards the end of 1941, the Board authorised the erection of a new two-storey building next to the still house in Point Pleasant. This freed space to extend the machine shop as well as accommodating the extended staff.

The substantial increase in works staff did not take place without criticism. In the autumn of 1941, Peter Seligman, with Whitlock present, proposed a further scheme of works reorganisation. Considerable development had taken place since 1936 and the organisation was simply unable to cope with the volume and complexity of the work. Wilson, however, pointed out that the works staff had increased already and he reckoned that the company had not benefited as it should. Nevertheless, he supported the proposals and they were adopted.

By the end of the war, labour relations had got very bad. It was even rumoured that a strike was to be called in one of the shops. This was attributed in some degree to faults in management but more to the wages situation. The workforce had been used to getting pay well above the average in industry. Then there had come two national awards, negotiated by the Engineering Employers' Federation with the unions, that wiped out the difference. This caused a lot of bad feeling.

Seligman met the shop stewards personally to explain the

position. It was then suggested that a committee consisting of representatives of workers and management should be set up so that such questions could be discussed. The first meeting of this Standing Consultative Committee, the forerunner of the later Joint Production Advisory Committee, took place in September 1945.

There were also changes in works management. Whitlock had joined the Board in 1942 and in 1945 R. M. ('Bob') May who had previously been Machine Shop Foreman and then Works Superintendent was appointed Works Manager.

The company's turnover rose steadily from £591,000 in 1940 to a peak of £1,031,000 in 1943 falling back to £942,000 in 1945. In comparing these figures with earlier ones, a substantial measure of inflation must be allowed for. The increase in turnover was not so substantial in real terms. The licence income, £5,500 in 1940, decreased partly because fees from Holstein und Kappert were cut off and partly from the reduction in royalty rate from York.

Profit followed a somewhat similar course to turnover, rising from £61,000 in 1940 to £182,000 in 1943 and falling back to £112,000 in 1945. A good deal of this was taken back through excess profit taxes of one kind or another, but it was still possible to pay dividends of 25% free of tax. The fair value of the shares rose substantially. It was fixed at £4 15s (£4.75) for 1940 and then, after much argument in the Board and a number of outside opinions, at £6 3s (£6.15) for 1941. It rose to £8 for 1943 and was finally fixed at £9 when the public issue was made in 1946. From then on the shares found their value on the open market and not from an evaluation by the Board.

The extra turnover required more working capital to finance it. In the main this was obtained by bank overdraft which was equal to more than four times the issued capital at the end of 1945. Wilson's prophecy at the beginning of the war had been amply justified. It was clear that the company was badly under-capitalised.

The position was made worse by the growth of work in progress, not just in monetary terms but in relation to turnover, a measure, albeit a crude one, of the speed with which work was being got through the shops. At the end of 1940 the ratio of sales to work in progress was about 6 but by 1942 it had fallen to 3.3 and remained at this level until the end of 1945.

The Board discussed this situation on a number of occasions. As early as the autumn of 1939, public flotation of the company at a propitious time had been agreed as a matter of general policy. By the end of 1945, the possibility of finding a number of new shareholders and keeping the company private was discussed but, by then, public flotation had become inevitable and was agreed early in 1946.

In 1943, a change of name to The A.P.V. Company Limited was considered but not supported by the sales managers and was therefore dropped. It was finally adopted in 1948.

The general efficiency of production was giving concern. The turnover per £1 paid in wages fell from about £6 at the start of the war to as little as £4 8s in 1943, but recovered to about £5 in 1945. Wages were increasing; the piece-work rate for a coppersmith was now 2s 7¼d (13p) an hour. So were salaries and what with the increase in the number of staff, overheads were outstripping both estimates and recovery.

On the Board, the disagreement between Wilson and the rest of the Directors got steadily worse; even though his agreement was renewed for five years from April 1940 and he was playing a dominant role in financial and sales policy. The first major rift occurred early in 1941 over an agreement with Peter Seligman appointing him Production Manager. Wilson, prompted no doubt by deeper jealousies than he was prepared to admit, was critical of Peter's ability to handle the production side where admittedly both Seligman and he had failed. He prophesied that this side of the business would have to be 'relinquished to a hard-bitten professional after the war'. All the same, he would not oppose the appointment and would do his best to make it work.

Seligman's feelings were now very bitter. He believed that since

1935 the business had grown beyond Wilson's capacity to manage, that he tried to bully his staff and that he had 'wrought atrocious injuries' on Seligman and his work. He was determined to press on with Peter's agreement which was accordingly adopted by the Board at its April meeting. Wilson's disapproval was minuted and the Chairman took full responsibility for the appointment.

Although once again relations had been patched up, too much had been said, with some justice on both sides, for any accommodation to be permanent. By March 1942, Seligman recorded that the Board had lost confidence in Wilson and wished to part with him as soon as possible.

When it was suggested that Whitlock should be invited to join the Board, Wilson opposed the appointment. Whitlock was duly elected in the spring of 1942, however.

The long drawn out drama was now reaching its close. Although in July Wilson was instructed by the Board to study the transition from war to peacetime conditions, the effect of the dissensions was being felt by at least the senior staff. Several of them were sending complaints of Wilson's behaviour to Seligman and, worse still, he was accepting them behind Wilson's back.

In the middle of the year, Wilson gave notice of his intention to dispose of his shares. Most of the shares were taken up by the Board but then the rest were bid for by the Pearl Assurance Co. Ltd at well above the fair value, provided they were given a seat on the Board. After much discussion this proposition was rejected and the additional shares were distributed among the members of the Board.

At the meeting where this was decided, Wilson suggested, and it was accepted, that his service agreement be cancelled and that he be employed on a part-time basis on terms that compensated him for loss of office. The formalities were completed in November but the new arrangement had no time to operate, for Seligman, after consulting the company's solicitors, had terminated Wilson's employment on the spot on 2 December. He left that afternoon. Two days later the Board met and confirmed the Chairman's action. They also elected Baigent to take his place on the Board.

It then appeared that the Board had acted improperly for the Articles of Association provided no grounds, other than bankruptcy or lunacy, for discharging a Director. The Articles had to be altered to legalise, if that were possible, this Gilbertian situation.

In 1943, the Board decided to appoint an outside Financial Director; they may well have been missing Wilson's sound commercial sense. Eventually, L. H. Davies, a chartered accountant, became Financial Adviser until the Annual General Meeting of 1946, after the company had gone public, when he joined the Board.

During the period some 2,200 further shares were issued, mainly to the Executive Directors. There was also a considerable redistribution of holdings consequent on the re-allotment of Wilson's shares and transfer of other shares leading to a number of new shareholders, all within the existing families.

Up to 1943 the Board had allocated a sum roughly equal to 15–20% of the previous year's profit for staff bonus to be distributed in conjunction with the departmental managers as they saw fit. This arbitrary scheme gave rise to a lot of discontent. It had, however, always been a cherished object of Seligman's to see that all his workpeople had a share in the profits of the company. In this he underestimated the difficulty of devising a fair and simple scheme and exaggerated the stimulus that such a scheme would give, especially to junior staff.

A scheme was proposed to allocate a similar proportion of profits but to distribute it to all salaried staff on a scale roughly proportional to basic salary. This was put into operation as from the beginning of 1943. As this was a year of unexpectedly high profit, the gratified staff were astonished at receiving bonuses in 1944 that amounted to a very substantial proportion of their total pay.

A new apprentice scheme, in which Crosby played a prominent part, was set up in mid-1943. A Staff Advisory Committee was set up in the summer of 1945 to deal with relations between staff and management, welfare, conditions of employment and so on. Towards the end of 1942, a medical department was established under a remarkably capable person, Sister Thorpe. A subsidised canteen was established. It was hardly a gourmet's Mecca but at a time of strict rationing it provided valuable extra nourishment.

There were a number of changes in senior staff. The most serious loss was the death of Percy Williams in February 1942, at the age of 69. He was working, apparently just as usual, until, a day or two before he died, he went home and faded away from pneumonia. It seemed that he would be irreplaceable but after a year, a modest but impressive individual, G. H. ('George') Botham, was engaged. He was a Yorkshireman, a chemist of the old school, who had had experience in agricultural chemistry before he came to APV. He was exactly the man the company needed, wide in his interests, profound and penetrating in analysis, with a strong sense of humour and unswervingly loyal. It was only a short time before he had made an enviable reputation as an authority on corrosion, first inside and then beyond the company.

Following Williams' death, Dummett had become Laboratory Manager.

T. E. French's agreement was terminated in November 1940 on the same day as Wyatt's; he was already near to retiring age. W. E. Crosby took his place as Chief Engineer, and Hugh Goodman became Chief Designer.

From quite early in the war, the Board had been considering post-war policy, particularly the recovery of the company's export markets to which they gave first priority. It was realised that the principal problems would be finance, manufacturing facilities, marketing organisation and adequate staff.

Apart from finance, one thing seemed clear; the facilities at Wandsworth, though they might be extended somewhat, would not suffice to meet the demands for production that looked certain to develop as soon as the war was over. In the autumn of 1944, it was decided to investigate the possibilities of moving to a new location out of London.

Given adequate finance and production resources, however, would the company have to look to new industries, materials and products in the future, or could it continue with the steady development of the lines that had served it so well up to 1939? Certainly, development had fallen severely behind as a result of the war. A number of patents had been filed but mostly they were either the result of pre-war development or, like those on distillation processes, aimed at specific war needs.

A primary concern for the future was the Chemical Engineering Department. On the one hand, it had developed new plant and processes and penetrated new industries, but on the other there was serious doubt about the ability of its management, especially as Ralph would be nearing retirement age at the end of the war.

Towards the end of 1943, Ralph presented a memorandum on the department. This suggested a substantial possible turnover and profit of at least £120,000 per annum. He foresaw much of this turnover in the processing of coal carbonisation by-products and in the cellulose acetate industry. After much discussion, the Board decided to authorise development on these lines provided that the department's organisation was stiffened and a suitable understudy to Ralph found and trained. Neither they nor Ralph foresaw – how could they? – that market forces were going to make nonsense of Ralph's predictions over the next few years.

Towards the end of the war, the company began to get interested in the pharmaceutical industry, particularly penicillin, then manufactured in this country by the hopelessly inefficient bottle culture method. To look after this side of the Chemical Engineering Department's work, F. E. ('Ned'), now Sir Frederick, Warner was recruited.

By 1944, the end of the war was in sight and development directed to the war effort had come to an end. The company was able to start work on peace-time projects. The first to be looked at was the heat exchanger. The advent of the HTST process had eliminated the holder plants. There was a resultant demand, on the one hand, for small units to replace the batch pasteuriser and, on the other, for increased throughputs of the larger machines to take full advantage of the process in large dairies. At the same time there was a growing requirement for all stainless steel units not just for appearance sake but to allow the use of cleaning agents that would corrode less resistant materials.

Work had started on this but had been stopped by the war. In the meantime, competition had grown. Sales of the new Alfa-Laval machine to several industries had already started. Clearly development of new machines had to be pushed ahead as fast as possible.

The work on a replacement for the HL was taken up again and in the summer of 1945 a new HM plate was already under test in a London dairy. It was pressed from a single stainless sheet and plates were spaced from each other by pressed 'pips'. The troughs were simple horizontal ones across the plate which was capable of considerably higher heat transfer coefficients than the HS or HL. To take advantage of this required the use of higher pressure drops so the machine had to be designed to work at higher pressures. A new design of frame clad in stainless steel sheet and capable of withstanding double the pressure of the HL was designed. As a result, the throughput that could be accommodated in a single frame went up from 1,500 to 2,000 gallons per hour HTST. An all-stainless steel, integral filter was also designed.

For smaller dairies, an HTST unit with capacities up to 400 gallons per hour was designed around an extended version of the HT.

With these developments, a requirement grew up for stainless steel castings. They had to be reliable in quality and not too difficult to machine. Those that were obtainable on the open market proved to be neither. A development programme was set up in the laboratory in conjunction with the foundry to determine the factors governing the quality of stainless steel castings and how they could be applied. Promising results were obtained, a small induction furnace was put down at Allsop's Wharf and, before long, castings were being produced consistently better than any otherwise available. Thus the know-how, on which eventually the APV-Paramount business was built up, was obtained the hard way by the application of first principles.

A new juice de-aeration and pasteurisation plant was tested in Palestine. This provided the basis for a standard plant that was to prove highly successful especially with citrus juices which up to this time had given difficulties.

In the coal tar refining field new possibilities were being explored. Following the success of the big toluene plant at Provanmill, the fractionation of coal tar acids to yield pure phenol (carbolic acid) and cresols was investigated and provided the basis on which a number of complex plants were later successfully put to work.

So APV moved into the post-war period better equipped to face the difficulties of the transition from a war-time economy than it had been twenty-five years before. Nevertheless, the next few years were to prove a difficult and testing time, for the problems to be tackled were different in kind from those faced in the early 1920s.

## Chapter 8

# APV Goes Public
# 1945–1951

The Second World War was to prove a bigger watershed for the company than had the first. Then, contrary to expectation, the business picked up very much as it had been before 1914 and, except for the financial crisis of 1919/20, developed on the Wandsworth site well within the company's own resources.

After 1945, however, the changes imposed by the war were such that there could be no simple return to pre-war conditions. There were several reasons for this. The company had already expanded physically beyond the capacity of the Point Pleasant site and there was every sign that it would expand further. At the same time the financial resources now required exceeded the capability of a family board to provide them. The number of employees had grown beyond that able to be managed on the earlier paternalistic basis. However regrettable it might seem to many, those old days had gone for good even though there was a substantial caucus of older employees who still regarded the firm as they had always done, so that attitudes took many years to change. Nevertheless, from this time on, the primary loyalty had to be to the company rather than to a person, however affectionately he might still be regarded and however little this change of outlook might be realised at the time.

Great social changes were taking place. The country had just won a terrible war. Most people felt that they could now slack off a bit and that they were due for some reward for the labours and tribulations of the past six years. It was not surprising that productivity suffered. Although rationing of food and clothing was

117

to remain for several years more, it was not yet clear to the general populace what an enormous drain on the national resources the war had been. Still less clear was it that there was a peace to be won as well as a war. A Labour Government had been returned with an overwhelming majority, the Welfare State and nationalised industries were being set up, wages and salaries were increasing in a way that could not have been contemplated a decade earlier and euphoria was general.

As far as manufacturing industry was concerned the position was unhealthy. The demand for goods, pent-up for so many years, was immense so that a typical seller's market developed. Delivery times were very long, a matter of years for anything but the simplest goods. There were shortages of fuel and of basic materials. Prices became of secondary importance with the result that all sorts of inefficiencies began to be tolerated and standards began to suffer. APV could not remain immune from such influences.

The position in the home markets was exacerbated by the necessity to increase exports. Overseas sales and the development of a marketing organisation to handle them became a first priority. Finally, now that the basic heat exchanger patents were nearing the end of their lives, competitors were starting to enter a field in which the company had, until then, held a virtual monopoly.

The whole industrial and political atmosphere had altered radically and it would take time to absorb the changes. But changes there had to be. The most urgent for APV was a reconstruction of the financial basis of the company.

During the war, the working capital for expansion of the business had been obtained by bank borrowing, the possibilities of substantially increasing reserves being prevented by taxation, particularly the excess profit tax. As a result, by the end of 1945, bank overdraft and loans amounted to five times the nominal issued capital. Clearly more outside capital was needed.

Early in 1946, a public flotation was decided on and the conditions for a share issue were being discussed with Seligman Brothers. On 7 February the Board agreed to increase the authorised share capital from £60,000 to £750,000 by issuing 400,000, £1, 4½% preference shares, by dividing each of the existing £1 ordinary shares into ten 2s shares and authorising the issue of further 2s shares up to a total of £750,000. The official Capital Issues Committee agreed in April to the share issue at 21s (£1.05) for the preference and 18s (90p) for the ordinary shares. On 2 May 1946 an Extraordinary General Meeting was held at which it was approved that the company go public. The share issue was entirely successful.

Thus the Aluminium Plant and Vessel Company became public[1] and received an input of about £315,000 in outside capital, enough to wipe out the bank loans but by no means enough to supply the capital needs of the company over the next few years. The increase in turnover, expenditure on new premises, investment in subsidiary companies and, above all, the ever-increasing lock-up in work in progress were all to make very heavy demands on its financial resources that were to lead eventually to a crisis whose consequences were to be at least as far reaching as those that occurred after the First World War.

But that was some years ahead. From 1946 to 1951 sales steadily increased from less than £0.9 million to over £2.8 million and with them profit, dividends, wages, overheads, work in progress, orders in hand and loans. There were, it is true, disturbing signs beyond problems of cash flow. In early 1946 there was a serious shortage of labour so that the hours being worked were substantially less than they had been a year before. At the same time, overheads were going up and at one time it looked as if the firm was going to make a loss in its first year as a public company. Productivity had caused concern for some time, although the introduction of a productivity bonus did something to alleviate matters.

However, reasonably satisfactory results were obtained considering all the shortages of raw materials and components. But then came an unexpected blow. The winter of 1946/7 was one of the coldest on record. In February 1947 there was a virtual collapse

[1]Its name was altered to The A.P.V. Company Limited in February 1948.

in power supplies and factories all over the country had to close down. The Wandsworth works was shut down for three weeks. The workforce was paid on a thirty-four-hour guaranteed week and lost a good deal of extra pay, but no staff were laid off. This came at a particularly bad time as, only a month before, the five-day week had been introduced.

By the end of 1947, the effect of the bonus was being felt and from then on productivity improved. The pound was devalued by about 40% in the autumn of 1949. This brought in, as it was intended to, a spate of overseas orders but increased the inflationary pressure on wages and salaries as well as raw material prices.

While sales and profits were growing, the company looked healthy enough, but all was not well. Put in financial terms the capital employed was growing much faster than sales. The ratio of capital to sales rose from 1.0 in 1945 to nearly 1.7 in 1951, though the profit on capital employed remained at about 17% from 1947 to 1951.

Put in simple terms the company was steadily expending more than it was receiving. Partly this was due to money expended on buildings and in the subsidiary companies but in the main it was caused by the enormous increase in stock and work in progress which had risen steadily from little over £¼ million at the end of 1945 to over £2 million by the end of 1951.

Difficulties in supply of material and lack of production space had much to do with this situation, so had poor productivity and control. Nevertheless, it is clear that, for several years on end, orders booked had substantially exceeded shipments from the shops. The seller's market had taken its toll. The Board was well aware of all this but was, in the event, powerless to take decisive action short of cutting down the scale of the company's sales activity and they were unwilling to contemplate that.

They were, nevertheless, faced by the necessity to provide the capital to finance this situation. They looked to borrowing of one kind or another rather than to making economies.

Public flotation in 1946 had provided enough new money to eliminate the bank overdraft. Nevertheless, in 1947 this had risen so far that the Board was urgently considering raising further capital. It was decided to issue another 100,000, £1, 4½% cumulative preference shares at 22s (£1.10). This enabled the position to be held for a couple of years but with a substantial overdraft.

The demand for more capital continued. In mid-1948, the short term loan facility from Seligman Brothers was increased. By then it was clear that the reduction of debt would be further delayed. Payments to Australia worsened the position but the Board was able to hold on until early 1950 when the prospect of having to finance moving the company to a new site, now decided to be at Crawley, forced them to take action.

After consultation, it was decided to increase the issued share capital. At the same time, some of the revenue reserve was capitalised and issued in the form of ordinary shares to existing shareholders in the ratio of 4 to 1 and the 2s ordinary shares were consolidated into nominal 10s shares. The following issue of 750,000 new 10s shares at 15s (75p) a share brought in some £560,000 of new money. In spite of this an overdraft remained and work in progress was still increasing.

During 1951 the estimated requirements for the Crawley project increased, money was required for the new subsidiaries and still more working capital was needed.

Eventually it was agreed that it would be advisable for a 'rights' issue of shares to accompany a loan stock issue. Accordingly late in 1951 the Board authorised the issue of 500,000 new ordinary shares to be made available in the ratio 1 to 3 to existing shareholders at 15s 6d (78p) together with £650,000 of 4¾% unsecured loan stock 1957/61 to be placed, mainly with institutions, at 99%. Seligman Brothers were charged with placing the issues and they went reasonably well.

These brought in a little over £1 million and put the company safely in the black. Seligman, in his Chairman's statement for 1951, however, stated 'your Directors are in no doubt that all your company's resources will be needed and fully employed before the end of 1952.' This was to prove a notable understatement.

Then, in 1951, came a further crisis. As a result of the armaments required for the Korean war, world-wide shortages had arisen in a number of key raw materials, notably nickel, molybdenum and columbium, all essential ingredients of the stainless steel that now formed the basis of most of APV's production. These and others like zinc, copper and aluminium, were all supposedly controlled as to price and quantity by the Ministry of Supply. Skilful buying combined with the allocation of most of the company's production to priority classes saved the situation from becoming catastrophic. It came, however, at a most unwelcome moment when expenditure on the new factory at Crawley was just starting to build up. The worst effects were not felt until the next year, nor did they prove as bad as was anticipated, but crash research and development programmes were initiated, aimed at finding substitute materials that would conserve the scarce metals.

## Development

The development of the company's products proceeded apace. The new all-stainless steel HM heat exchanger was already getting into production in 1945. For pasteurisation duties, a packaged plant with all auxiliaries, also in stainless steel, was developed, the so-called Panel plant.

The HM Panel was rushed out so that it could be shipped to Stockholm for the Dairy Show there in May 1946, when the new APV-Nordiska subsidiary company was inaugurated, but it made less impact on the chauvinistic Swedes than the new Alfa-Laval machine then just coming on the market. Nevertheless, it was a handsome machine and, initially, it sold well. It was the first genuine all-stainless steel plant, for the foundry at Allsop's Wharf was now producing castings for fittings and for a new readily cleaned pump patented during the war.

It was unfortunate, then, that after such a good start, the HM should have been dogged with misfortune. The major difficulty proved both serious and baffling. After the machine had been on the market for about a year, C. H. ('Charles') Brissenden, who had been engaged in the laboratory as assistant to Botham to investigate dairy problems, detected signs of corrosion on the pips of the heat exchanger plates. It was soon established that this was something previously unheard of, severe corrosion of stainless steel by untreated milk. Further investigation showed that the corrosion was relatively general and occurring on a number of plants. It looked as if all the plates so far installed were at risk and would have to be replaced.

The future of the HM was at stake but all was not lost. Botham carried out a remarkably rapid and imaginative piece of research which showed conclusively that the attack was the result of 'fretting', a form of corrosion never before reported in liquid media.

Fortunately, a relatively minor modification that prevented the fretting could be made and carried out on plates in service but a considerable programme of plate replacements was involved.

As ill luck would have it, there was another mishap about this time. A plate machine in Holland blew up and the tightening bar was fired out of the frame like a projectile, doing a lot of material damage but fortunately hurting no one. There could have been a fatal accident, so a quick solution was essential. The cause of failure was clear at first glance. Failure had occurred by complete disintegration of the bronze bush carrying the tightening spindle.

There was no question of this being underdesigned. An investigation showed that failure was due to inter-granular corrosion of the bronze. But what could be the corrosive agent? Eventually it was shown that it was minute traces of ammonia in the atmosphere derived from hardly perceptible leaks from a refrigeration plant, something that could happen on any dairy plant.

All the bronze bushes that were in operation had to be replaced forthwith, a costly programme that took some months to complete. This prompt action did, however, do something to recover the goodwill lost by the other misfortunes.

For the smaller dairies, the HTC, a new small heat exchanger incorporating HT plates, was on the market towards the end of 1946. A few months later, standard pasteurisation plants based on it were available. At the same time, a modified version of the plate with a wider gap and deeper gaskets was put out to handle liquids with a higher solids content, particularly citrus juices containing cells, and so allowed the company access to this important market.

By 1949, the dairy industry was seeking equipment which could operate at higher temperatures and pressures especially for the preheating of milk at high temperature before sterilising. Tests were started on an HM reinforced to withstand 60 psi pressure to heat milk momentarily to 265°F (130°C). By 1951 it had been shown that the process was feasible and that reasonably long runs could be attained, although the life of the rubbers then available was, not surprisingly, unacceptably short. Thus started the work that was to lead to the ultra high temperature processes of today.

Demands for machines to withstand more arduous conditions were coming from several sources such as the wood pulp industry where a survey had shown that the opportunity for plate heat exchangers was immense. Plate machines would, however, have to be more robust, larger and able to resist higher temperatures and pressures than the existing range. It was ruled, however, that effort must be concentrated on meeting demands from the existing dairy, brewery and food markets.

It was now clear that there was a considerable demand for a more robust and effective machine than the HM. Early in 1949 Goodman had patented a plate with deep horizontal troughs across it into the walls of which were pressed small subsidiary corrugations. This would both be more rigid and, because of the large number of accelerations and decelerations of flow, possess higher heat transfer capability than the HM. It would also be easier to press.

This was a first-class idea that was to lead to the HX and HMB, two of the most successful plates APV ever produced, but it was decided to apply it first to a larger machine aimed at applications in the chemical industry. This was the HF, launched in the autumn of 1951.

It was designed to withstand pressures up to 120 psi and a temperature of 130°C, to handle flows up to 40,000 gallons per hour and to carry larger particles in suspension by doubling the plate gap.

It looked a good machine and quite a number were sold, but it was never a great success. Too much was given away in heavy gauge material to gain robustness and in the wide gap, both of which badly decreased thermal efficiency. It was not a bad solution to the problem, but a better and more radical one was to be found a year or two later.

In 1948, a major development was made, the introduction of expanded stainless steel pipe fittings, the now familiar RJT fitting. Up to 1947 fittings had been in nickel bronze or tinned gunmetal sweated or brazed to the pipe, usually of tinned copper. In 1947, stainless steel fittings welded to the pipe were introduced but it was not until the expanded fitting was available that it became a generally saleable item. The development demanded a lot of careful design and production engineering. Bends, tees and a new and attractive design of cock were included in the range so that for the first time in Britain complete product lines with all-stainless steel contact could be made up meccano-wise. A special shop had to be equipped for their production.

The RJT fitting was an immediate success and has remained so. It became a British Standard and has proved, so far, to be the most popular ever produced in this country. Even in 1949, the sales totalled some £190,000 and output rose steadily thereafter.

A highly successful innovation, second only in importance to the heat exchanger, though it did not seem so at first, was just being started at this time. The plate evaporator in its initial form was a series of circular plates fed through a pipe in the centre and heated by steam between them. The liquid was spread as a film over the surface by the vapour evolved as it passed out with the concentrate to the periphery. This was Goodman's first conception and it was found to be only very partially successful. Not until it was realised that it was impossible to wet an expanding area of surface with a

125

decreasing volume of liquid could real progress be made. This, however, was some years ahead.

The work on cream deodorising in a current of steam that had to be dropped during the war was restarted. Experiments in New Zealand were disappointing but at the same time a similar two-spray column unit was successfully put to work in Belgium. So, even though there was still a long way to go in New Zealand, the company at last had some reward for twelve years' labour and the unit was able to be marketed on the Continent.

The shortage of raw materials gave rise to much metallurgical work first in the laboratory and then in the works. For the most part it was aimed at nickel saving. A very interesting general purpose alloy was worked out and patented. It was ductile, easily cast, weldable and with corrosion resistance comparable to the 18/8 austenitic steels. No one was interested in it, however, not even the foundry's customers, and the crisis was over before a first-class piece of development could be tried out in practice.

Immediately after the war there began the most far-reaching development in welding since the company was founded, the 'argon arc' process. Until then welding had been exclusively by oxyacetylene, oxycoal gas or metallic-arc, in each case with a flux. Now the use of a tungsten arc, adding filler metal in an argon gas atmosphere to prevent oxidation instead of flux, a method first invented in America, was proposed. APV was one of the first companies in Britain to try out the process. The main advantages were clear: no flux, high welding speed, very neat, strong welds requiring little finishing and suitability for automatic welding.

In mid-1946, it was being developed for stainless steel. Three years later, automatic welding of stainless steel pipelines and fittings was in operation.

By 1951, the process had been developed for tanks and vessels in stainless steel, copper and aluminium, and its dependability and economy proved. From now on 'argon-arc' in its various forms was to oust gas as the basic method of welding in APV.

## Marketing

In the company's main markets there had been big changes following the war. There were now many more competitors, especially overseas, in its specialised fields. Mergers and amalgamations were reducing the number but increasing the size and power of its customers. They became tougher to sell to and some of them were developing their own engineering facilities and so were becoming less inclined to leave it to companies like APV to do development for them. It became necessary to develop the firm as process engineers and contractors for complete installations as well as to seek new and improved equipment.

The seller's market was beginning to change in 1949 but the enormous backlog and order book was to continue for some years longer. It had already dislocated some markets. In 1946, Thomas was reporting a demand for some 280 HM machines in the Scandinavian market, but it was only possible to allot 120 machines. This failure to be able to deliver, the difficulties with the new machine and the rising competition from Alfa-Laval were together to cost APV the Swedish dairy market.

Nevertheless, the dairy business as a whole was going great guns. By 1950, when the post-war sales pattern had established itself, dairying accounted for about half the business, over a third of this being exported. There were a number of spectacular orders overseas. First there were thirty-five installations supplied to UNICEF (United Nations International Children's Emergency Fund) to meet the needs of countries on both sides of the Iron Curtain whose food production had been disrupted by the war and its aftermath. This was followed in 1950 by the Lisbon Central Dairy and the great Aarey dairy scheme that was in essence a complete reorganisation of the milk supply to Bombay. In these the company supplied complete installations for handling, pasteurising and bottling city supplies of liquid milk.

It was at this time, too, that Jack Matthews started a series of overseas tours, mainly to the English-speaking parts of the world, that quickly established him as a dairy sales engineer of international repute. It was recognised by his being elected President of the recently formed Society of Dairy Technology for 1947/8. This was a remarkable achievement, for before the war he had been no more than a junior salesman.

At home a large number of complete installations were made in dairies up and down the country, some of them very large and complex. The Cricklewood depot of Express Dairies had the highest throughput of any dairy at that time (1949). Nevertheless, milk production was overhauling consumption and it was clear that before long there would be a surplus for the manufacture of products – condensed milk, milk powder, cream, ice-cream mixes, butter and cheese – for which plant would be needed.

One piece of equipment that APV lacked was an homogeniser, not of much value in the home market where homogenised milk has never been popular but often required overseas. At the end of 1950, an agreement was signed with G. & J. Weir of Glasgow to market their homogeniser in all overseas countries. The venture did not prove very successful but it gained the company a foot in the market and paved the way for future developments.

In the brewery industry there was also a great upsurge in work. New installations and even replacements had been almost halted by the war. The demand for stainless steel plant was growing rapidly, so was the size of breweries, while the new argon-arc welding process was peculiarly well suited to the manufacture of large vessels on site. There was a substantial inflow of business, mainly for fermenters, heat exchangers and Scott yeast plants, much the same pattern as before the war.

Before stainless steel could be generally accepted in British breweries it had to be demonstrated. In 1946, the first fermenting vessel was installed and proved highly successful. From then on stainless steel became the preferred material as far as supply would allow.

The manufacture of stainless steel fermenters continued unabated but copper was by no means finished. Several complete brew-houses were supplied. There was also an order for an enormous battery of seventy-one 140-barrel fermenters, almost the last big installation of copper fermenters to be built by APV.

The HM was proved for brewery operation most successfully. By early 1950, HMs were installed in over thirty breweries in the British Isles. Guinness had ordered twenty-six at once for Dublin and a battery of four was being installed at Tuborg in Copenhagen, an important break into the exclusive continental lager market.

Patsy Norman retired in 1945. His place as Manager of the Brewery Engineering Department was taken by Bill Paine. He did not prove an apt manager. His interest was in development, not in running an effective and profitable sales organisation. By 1950 it was clear that he would have to be replaced. In December of that year, E. G. ('Eric') Watson, who had been Plant Manager of the big alcohol dehydration plant at Hammersmith when it was started up in 1938, took over as Manager at the end of 1951 and Paine was transferred to Research and Development as Brewery Research Engineer.

In the Chemical Engineering Department (CED) things were to go very differently from the way Ralph had prophesied to the Board in his war-time memorandum. At first all went well. At Courtaulds, expansion of cellulose acetate production had been decided on. This would involve not only acetic acid recovery units but plants for the manufacture of acetic acid and acetic anhydride and cellulose acetylating drums, all in corrosion resistant materials.

The recovery of pure chemicals from the tars and benzoles derived from coal carbonisation using APV processes was also already developing.

There was scope, too, for alcohol distillation, though not at home. A stroke of an administrative pen had doubled the output of every fermentation alcohol plant in the country. Before the war, the excise authorities prohibited the distillation of alcohol at the same time that fermentation was proceeding on the same site. Plants were therefore designed to ferment half the week and distil the other half. During the war, this was rescinded and it was possible to use the fractionating columns truly continuously, thus doubling the output.

All this was to change and change fast, though no one at APV realised it at this time. Basically the cause was the huge expansion in supply of cheap oil on which a petrochemical industry could be based. Before 1945 the only petrochemical plant existing in Britain was that of British Celanese at Spondon, near Derby, based on the thermal cracking of gas oil, and this only went to work in 1942. In 1947, however, the Anglo-Iranian Oil Company, now BP, and DCL jointly founded British Hydrocarbon Chemicals Ltd at Grangemouth to produce, amongst other chemicals, alcohol via ethylene. This was vastly cheaper than the fermentation product. Since then, no new fermentation industrial alcohol plant has been put down in Britain nor, as a result, has there been any extension of the chemical industry based on it.

So finished one of Ralph's dreams. The tar industry was also largely doomed, but it took longer to dwindle. Tar and benzole are by-products of the production of coke and gas by coal carbonisation. Economy in coke usage in blast furnaces, and the replacement of coke by oil and gas for heating in offices and homes, has meant that the demand for coke has been almost static. The replacement of coal gas, first by gas produced from naphtha reforming and then by North Sea methane, stopped the old fashioned gas works in a year or two in the 1960s. The quantity of tar and benzole was greatly reduced as a result and the demand for new processing plant almost vanished over about fifteen years from 1945.

But there was still the Courtaulds' work. By mid-1946 the largest order that APV had ever received, for an acetic acid recovery plant, was announced. Ralph certainly looked on this as a first instalment and arrangements were made for a visit to Germany under the Technical Reparations Scheme to get full information on the processes to be applied.

In the meantime, however, disaster had overtaken Ralph. First he had learned that Courtaulds intended to undertake the engineering of the new plants themselves and fabrication would go to open tender. Then, sitting at his desk one afternoon in November 1946, he got the news that the order for the huge phosphor-bronze acetylating drums had not gone to APV. He glanced at the note, muttered, 'You have killed me,' and collapsed from a stroke that he was never to throw off.

The department was plunged into confusion. Ralph had never revealed to any of his assistants what was going on except very partially, so no one in the company knew the full position. Dummett was put in to hold the fort as best he could. In the late spring, Ralph returned and took on the managership again. But he was a shadow of himself, so that he had to be retired at the end of 1947. He died a year or two later.

Dummett took over the department temporarily when Ralph left, with some reluctance. In this he was justified. It is difficult now to imagine a sales department without a sales or profit target, no budget and no routine information about progress, costs or profitability on any job or even on the department as a whole. He could do no more than hold the department together, get enough orders to keep it viable and seek a permanent successor.

A successor proved hard to find but in the end Robin Edgeworth Johnstone was appointed. He was an excellent chemical engineer with experience in Kenya and the oil industry in Trinidad and in Britain. He held the post for a couple of years but resigned in June 1951 eventually to become a most successful Professor of Chemical Engineering at the University of Nottingham. He was succeeded by Bill Webb.

In spite of all the difficulties, the department continued to execute a number of substantial contracts. Several of these were for acetic acid recovery plants which were highly successful.

There were a number of novel alcohol units for potable spirits but the only major enquiry for industrial alcohol plant came from the Argentine. In 1948 the Government there required tenders for up to five large complete installations to provide fuel alcohol from waste maize including all auxiliaries such as boilers, electric generators and maize and alcohol handling plant. The value of each plant was over £1 million, say £8 million at present values. The company was urged by the British Government to quote and decided to do so. Bill Webb re-joined the company to supervise the project technically, and as representative in Buenos Aires. The British Government was setting out to negotiate a trade agreement with the Argentine and the alcohol plants were included in it. When a final tender was presented in 1949 it appeared that Argentina had not a farthing of British currency and the negotiations came to a full stop.

Installation of benzole and tar product plants continued unabated, including several large tar acid plants of novel design. Although they brought little, if any, work to the shops, such contracts were welcome at a time of excessive backlog just for that reason.

Oil and varnish plant continued to be an important part of CED business, in spite of the growing threat from synthetic oils and resins. The Sommer plants were improved and a number of complete installations undertaken, some of them overseas. All this, however, was a result of the immediate post-war demand. No work was being done to develop new plant and, as a result, this side of the business was going to be lost.

There was another side, however, that seemed to be developing fast, plant for the pharmaceutical industry. This was Ned Warner's particular responsibility. A number of units were supplied, including heat exchangers, pipelines and fittings, pumps and control gear, for the appallingly cumbersome bottle-culture penicillin plants.

At the beginning of 1947, Ned Warner was made manager of a new department to handle food, fruit juice, wine and pharmaceuticals. It gave him less scope as a chemical engineer than he had wanted and, after a year, he left eventually to join Cremer and

Warner, the distinguished consulting firm of which he became senior partner.

G. O. Inglis, who followed him, applied himself wholeheartedly to the food and soft drinks business and built it up unobtrusively and well. For the most part, the food plant was standard stuff but in 1950 an important development was started.

The pasteurising of liquid egg is a tricky process because of the ease with which the white albumen coagulates at the temperature required for pasteurising. A complete line, incorporating an HTC machine, was installed and experiments began. By the spring of 1941, full data had been obtained on which to design complete liquid egg treatment lines and this has been the basis of a standard APV product ever since.

The fruit juice business at last got launched. The de-aeration and pasteurisation plant sold well in many countries and for other juices besides citrus.

A full-size pilot tubular citrus juice evaporator was designed and installed in Palestine. Much, probably too much, was expected from it. It worked quite effectively but could not produce juice of much better than normal quality. This had to await the arrival of the plate evaporator ten years later.

Transport tanks in aluminium as well as stainless steel continued to go well. Total sales passed the million pound mark in 1947, substantial business amounting to more than a twelfth of the total company turnover since its foundation.

In the foundry there were radical changes both in the department and in its business. It lost two of its most experienced executives. Stanley, who had joined the company in 1914 and had built up the foundry from its very beginnings during the First World War, retired in November 1946. He was succeeded by Len Smith, a very astute salesman, without Stanley's deep knowledge of the business, but who did an excellent job until he was sent to India in 1950 when H. W. Keeble took his place. About the same time Fred Davis, who had been Foreman since 1916, but for a five-year gap in the 1920s, and had an enormous fund of knowledge of the craft of non-ferrous founding, retired.

Immediately after the war, there were a lot of cancelled war orders and the problem was to get work to fill the foundry. This was done but only by taking on many jobs that showed no profit and often did not cover overheads. Costs were high and productivity low. The volume of business was large, however, and, ridiculous as it might seem, the foundry had to take on extra men and run a night shift. Some of the work even had to be subcontracted.

By mid-1947, the market for castings was falling and competition was increasing. Productivity had been improved by the payment of a productivity bonus. However, the large backlog acted as a buffer against falling orders and better prices were secured so that 1947 was a much less disastrous year.

All this was in the non-ferrous business where practically the whole of production now had to be sold on the open market. Stainless steel castings, on the other hand, were all being used inside the company. The output from Allsop's Wharf was still small but there were now two small induction furnaces at work and the castings in free-machining steel were of excellent quality.

Then came a dramatic change in the APV foundry business. For some years, the Board had sought a site for a new foundry. Then, in August 1947, a Mr Black wrote out of the blue and asked if APV would take an interest in Paramount Alloys, a foundry firm in Slough making special stainless alloy castings. At first sight it hardly looked a good bet. On the first two years' operation they had lost £37,000, they had two electric furnaces on order that they could not pay for and their assets were valued at £12,000. But it was just what was needed for the development of the APV stainless steel founding business. Towards the end of the year it was acquired, lock, stock and barrel, as a subsidiary company.

Just exactly how much Paramount cost the company is uncertain, for there were large losses to set against tax. Baigent once estimated it at £7,000. The only definite figure is the asset value in the APV balance sheets from 1947 on – a beggarly £963.

It was soon discovered that Paramount's patented alloys were of no commercial value. They were worked out as quickly as possible and replaced by austenitic stainless steels based on the Wandsworth know-how. There was a lot of development to be done, so it was not until the new furnaces were installed and working in early 1949 that production overtook Allsop's and Slough was running at a profit. The output in 1950 was double that in 1949 and by the end of 1951 it had doubled again.

The workforce and staff nearly trebled over this period. Madron Seligman, Richard's youngest son who had just joined the company, was made a director of Paramount Alloys, along with Peter Seligman and Baigent, at the beginning of 1950 and he took charge when Smith was in India.

In the meantime, the main foundry at Wandsworth had been running into trouble. A severe recession in 1948 had led to laying off a number of semi-skilled and unskilled men although by the end of the year things were improving and so it continued, up and down, for the rest of this period.

Perhaps the most important expansion of the company at this time lay in the development of its export marketing net. The demand to export emanated from a Government that was desperately in need of foreign currency but it was readily accepted by a Board that, under Seligman's leadership, was already very internationally inclined. Certainly they never seem to have worried about expending money on foreign enterprises. As a policy, they favoured owning, or at least having a financial interest in, their main export outlets.

Exports increased rapidly in value. From some £60,000 in 1945 they jumped to £210,000 in 1946 and increased steadily to £860,000 in 1950 when they amounted to 37% of total sales.

It was soon clear that a separate export department was going to be needed at Wandsworth. Raymond Thomas was at the point of retirement and he would have to be replaced. The choice fell on P. N. ('Philip') Savory who joined the company towards the end of

1946. He was a genial, burly man whose interests were largely in flour milling. He did a useful job in establishing a formal export department but by the middle of 1951 he was being retained only for consultation one day a week.

In the meantime, R. M. D. ('Dick') Odgers, who had served with Madron Seligman in the war, had been engaged in 1947 as Savory's assistant. He was a very active and bright individual, though no engineer, and took over the Managership of the Export Department *de facto* in 1951.

In Europe, attention was first directed at Scandinavia, especially Sweden where much was expected of the new HM. There was grave doubt if Wedholm's, who had taken over Petersen's business, would prove satisfactory agents. Nevertheless, it was agreed to retain them as dairy selling agents for Sweden under the overall direction of a new subsidiary established in 1946, APV Nordiska AB, responsible for all sales and technical services in Scandinavia under Waleur Petersen as Managing Director.

APV Nordiska did not do well from the start. The volume of business to justify it did not develop in the face of fierce local competition and there was a tendency for it to undertake work that should have been done by its agents. It struggled on with changes of management and function until it was wound up in 1953.

Elsewhere in Europe, things went better, even though there were initially considerable Government restrictions on imports as a result of the war.

Business in France developed satisfactorily so, in 1950, the Paris office was converted to a subsidiary company, Société APV, to act as a technical selling organisation, marketing in France through its own staff and in the other countries through agents.

In Holland, Merkens did a remarkably good job immediately following the war. The initial goodwill was, however, largely dissipated in the following year by serious corrosion troubles which affected APV machines more than those of competitors who were by now getting back into a market that had been dominated by

APV. Although this was overcome, Merkens, who was now an ageing and sick man, became discouraged and lost touch with the market. By 1951 it was clear that much reorganisation would be needed.

In Italy, things moved slowly and it was the growth of fruit juice business that stimulated interest in this market. After a good deal of negotiation APV Italia-Ing.Marenghi and C.-SpA was established in April 1950 as a joint venture with an engineer named Marenghi (father of Giovanni Marenghi, the present Managing Director) as Managing Director but with financial control resting with APV.

Outside Europe, too, the export organisation was developing. The USA subsidiary, Walker-Wallace Inc., had become reasonably profitable during the war. Expansion both of turnover and profit continued after it and in the middle of 1947 the company moved to a new factory in Buffalo with Earl W. Hall as General Manager.

In 1950 the Board had decided that all plates must be exported from the UK and so the manufacturing licence with York would have to terminate when it expired two years later. In 1951, the company further strengthened its position by purchasing almost all K. L. Wallace's shares in the Buffalo company thus increasing its share to 96½%. In the upshot, the York sales agreement also lapsed and in 1952 Buffalo took over marketing APV equipment in the USA dairy industry.

Australia had always had close links with Wandsworth. Increasing business in the dominion served to make them closer. By 1948 there were some 350 APV heat exchangers operating in Australia and it was rightly felt that more fabricating support was needed.

At the end of that year it was decided to set up a new subsidiary company, APV Australia (Pty) Ltd, with most of the capital provided by APV, and John Bryant as Chairman. A sheet metal shop was established in Brisbane to manufacture tanks, evaporators and other bulky items that it was not economic to ship from Britain.

The new shop started operation at the end of 1949. From the start, although operations were reasonably profitable, there were difficulties with scarcities of essential materials and skilled labour. The imposition of import controls in 1951 only made things more difficult.

That year, the APV operation was merged with Bryant Brothers. APV acquired 51% of the shares in a holding company, APV (Australia) Bryant Pty. Ltd, that took over the share capital of both companies whose activities, however, remained much as they had been before the merger.

Things were going by no means so satisfactorily in India. Early in 1946 it was decided to go ahead with the new factory at Dum-Dum on the basis of optimistic sales forecasts. They were not realised and provision for losses had to be made in that year and the next. An attempt to float APVEC as a public company proved abortive and there were changes in management. Webb resigned at the end of 1947. His replacement was no more successful and eventually, two years later, Len Smith was sent out to take over.

In spite of all these troubles, the Board continued to support the Indian venture, if with some trepidation.

The factory was opened in the middle of 1947. It was very well equipped for an Indian shop and there were about a hundred work people by mid-1948. When it started up, there was grave worry about lack of orders. But APVEC was saved by one large contract for stainless and aluminium equipment for the great Sindri fertiliser plant, engineered by Power-Gas. Almost immediately afterwards, APV gained the contract for the Aarey (Bombay) Milk Scheme, so, by mid-1948, the problem was rather delivery than orders.

It seemed as if the corner had been turned but the difficulties were not yet over. It appeared that APVEC's chances of getting much industrial alcohol business, the original reason for founding the company, were small. Then the 1948 results again showed an unexpected loss.

In spite of these troubles, APVEC made a profit in 1949. In 1950 and 1951, conditions were difficult. There were communal disturbances, parts of the workforce disappeared overnight and it was not surprising that profitability was less. The order book had run down too. Nevertheless, it was felt that APVEC was at last in the clear.

Smith's appointment was only for two years. It was therefore necessary to find a replacement to take over from him at the end of 1951. The choice fell on Henry Pickard, a bluff but very good-hearted Yorkshireman who had had wide experience. He brought a fund of down-to-earth common sense into the company which he served well for fifteen years.

In 1949, a proposal to establish a joint sales and engineering sub-sidiary in Brazil with Landmann Filhos & Cia and with H. Felsberg of Landmann as full-time Managing Director was before the Board. This was to handle all APV products to all industries, not just dairy as hitherto. It was recognised that manufacturing facilities could well be needed later on. The APV share was to be 51% and the new company was formed at the beginning of 1950. W. S. Robinson left Paris, where he had been working under Lawless, to join it in Sao Paulo, where he remained, eventually to become Managing Director.

Within the next two years, substantial orders were obtained for dairy and brewery plant though there were difficulties in remitting profits.

### Premises and Personnel

The scale of turnover achieved during the war and in the years following meant that there could be no question of the Point Pleasant premises continuing to be able to accommodate the company's work. The major problem was a long-term one: should the company try to stay on the Wandsworth site, or should it undertake the difficult and dangerous course of moving to a new one?

With a good deal of courage the Board took the view that the firm must move. They were encouraged by the conviction that it would be virtually impossible to accommodate all the APV manufacturing requirements at Point Pleasant. In any case, the existing buildings were a hotch-potch that would require extensive rebuilding involving almost as much dislocation as moving.

It had been hoped that new premises could be found which would afford further space for extension but, when this fell through, it became urgently necessary to find an alternative. At the end of 1947, three rather dilapidated shops in the White City, the old 1908 exhibition site at Shepherds Bush, were rented for five years and by the end of 1948 some 40,000 square feet of useful space was coming into operation.

By 1949 the matter of a permanent site was getting urgent as the interim arrangements for temporary production facilities at the White City were due to lapse in a year or two and the staff was getting restive at the delays. After various false starts, the Board turned to the idea of Crawley in 1949 and, following a good deal of negotiation, a 99-year lease of the present location was signed on 28 April 1950. There were those who would have preferred a freehold property but the deciding factor was the Crawley Corporation's commitment to provide housing for the employees transferring there from London. The need to ensure that most of the company's skilled workforce and staff should move to a new place with it, had been a cardinal point in all considerations of new localities. Any move that resulted in loss of a substantial proportion of them would have been disastrous.

In the meantime, there was the necessity to provide sufficient shop space, however congested and inefficient, until the new factory was ready. The acquisition of Paramount Alloys went a long way towards relieving the pressure on the foundry and at Point Pleasant various *ad interim* extensions were made. The Garratt Lane shop was completely refitted and extended.

The offices were scattered all over the Wandsworth site; the drawing offices alone were in four different buildings. There were works offices, large and small, at each factory. No wonder that everyone from the Board down was looking to the Crawley development to overcome the inefficiencies inherent in so haphazard an organisation with its congestion and continual transfer of material and half-finished goods between the various shops. At last the company would be in a single place in buildings tailormade for its purposes.

The first objective was to erect a building to be ready early in 1952 to house the foundries, including Paramount, and the White City operations. The rest of the works and offices were to be transferred some six to eight years later.

Madron Seligman was put in charge of planning the Crawley development, backed by a team of engineers, under a Crawley committee consisting of Peter Seligman, Whitlock, Baigent and May as permanent members.

By October, the Board was informed that the first stage of the move was going to require capital expenditure of £750,000 instead of the £531,000 estimated earlier. The second stage was going to need £395,000 in place of £214,000 after disposing of the Wandsworth properties and assuming two-thirds of the cost of buildings financed by mortgage. It was also estimated that the new shop would handle a turnover of £3,000,000 per anum with increased profits and savings amounting to some £155,000. On this somewhat optimistic advice, the Board went ahead. They were too far committed to do much else.

By the end of 1950 plans were far advanced. It had now been decided that the first stage of the move should encompass practically all the shops except the coppersmiths' and blacksmiths' who would follow in stage 2 together with the office staff. The foundries would be amalgamated in a new subsidiary, A.P.V. Paramount Ltd, and would also be moved to a separate block as part of stage 1.

The foundry block was divided into two equal sections, one for stainless steel, the other for non-ferrous founding. The economics of staying in the non-ferrous foundry business were not questioned.

It was intended to level the site during the winter and start building in the spring so that the move of shops to Crawley could start in 1952. When stage 1 was complete, and the White City evacuated, the total area occupied by the company would be a third greater than when the operation started.

Personnel problems played a major part in the overall planning. Although a census of opinion amongst the employees had already shown that a very high proportion would be prepared to move with the company to Crawley if adequate housing were available, the company continued to make every effort to keep the employees fully informed.

At this time, too, the company made an astute move by purchasing Jordans, a Tudor farmhouse with a barn, tennis courts and field attached. Only three hundred yards from the factory site, it was ready-made as a social and sports club.

At the end of 1950, the building contract for the factory was laid but the winter weather was very bad so that, by the spring, work was two months behind schedule. Thereafter things went reasonably well but by the end of June the Board was once again faced with revised estimates.

At Wandsworth, immediately after the war, there had been an acute shortage of skilled labour but by mid-1946 this had ceased to be a serious problem. Much more alarming was the poor productivity of the shops. In part this was due to difficulties of supply, drawing office delays and the like, but in the main it rested in insufficient effort on the part of the workforce.

The Board had already set up a Standing Consultative Committee between management and works employees and had approved establishing a productivity hourly bonus scheme in 1945. The men were chary of supporting the committee so that no productivity bonus was being paid until the middle of the following year. The position was not helped by the advent of the five-day week. Nor did the standing committee exert itself to improve the very poor timekeeping or eliminate restrictive practices which had gained a hold in the works.

The shut-down due to the fuel crisis early in 1947 brought people to their senses. Timekeeping improved and productivity increased to a much more satisfactory figure. In 1947 and on, the production targets were met.

The production bonus substantially increased wage rates but there is little doubt that the policy was successful. The ratio of production value to productive wages rose steadily from 5.3 in 1946 to 7.6 in 1951, an increase of 43%. Relations between management and employees, which had deteriorated badly in 1945/6 also improved greatly.

In 1945 the decision was taken to appoint a Production Manager in the hopes that he would help to overcome the production difficulties. Then at the beginning of 1947, Bob May was appointed General Works Manager responsible to Whitlock as Works Director. He had recommended the appointment to the Board where there had been those who doubted if May, who had spent almost all his working life in the APV machine shop, had the breadth of knowledge and experience that would enable him to fill the post satisfactorily. However, it was decided that it was better not to make an outside appointment.

In 1945, the idea of the Welfare State was in the air. The new Government was busy implementing the Beveridge report and the time was ripe to put new social schemes into operation. Seligman was not backward in taking opportunities that accorded well with his natural inclinations.

The apprentice scheme was extended in scope and in 1950 a graduate training scheme was inaugurated. It was hoped that this would serve as a means of recruiting young people with management potential. In this it was not successful and after a few years the scheme was dropped. Its first member, however, unlike others later, did stay. He was D. T. ('David') Shore, who had served an apprenticeship with APV, then graduated from Imperial College in mechanical engineering, took an M.Sc. and is now Managing Director.

The total number of employees, mainly staff, did not increase greatly – 960 in 1939, 1,030 in 1943, 1,400 in 1951 – nothing like proportional to the increase in turnover.

Clouston, who had reached the age of 70, retired from the Board in 1950; Jack Matthews and Madron Seligman joined it at the beginning of 1951.

Madron was an Oxford arts graduate and had no engineering knowledge or experience. After leaving the university he was sent for a short time to get some experience of industry at Hall's of Dartford and in the USA before joining APV.

Richard Seligman received a number of signal distinctions. In 1945, he was awarded the Platinum Medal, the highest honour of the Institute of Metals of which he had been President for 1930–31, for services to metallurgy. In 1951 he was the first recipient of the Gold Medal of the Society of Dairy Technology, their highest award and rarely given, for services to the dairy industry.

In 1948 W. H. ('Bill') Jones, a most capable and loyal person who was to fill a number of difficult, not to say thankless jobs in the APV group over the next thirty years, was appointed Chief Draughtsman, while Hugh Goodman became Chief Engineer when Crosby gave up the post because of ill health at the end of 1949.

First steps were taken to set up a research and development organisation less centred on the Technical Director than before; Seligman was already over seventy. Dummett was appointed Scientific Manager and a Research and Development (R&D) Committee was established with Goodman, Dummett and Botham under Seligman as chairman. Its first task was to establish priorities among the various projects that had been launched haphazardly everywhere in the organisation.

The scientific development, in corrosion, welding and distillation processes for example, was carried out in the chemical, metallurgical and chemical engineering sections of the Laboratory under George Botham with J. F. ('Johnny') Lancaster as Chief Metallurgist.

The heart of the company's engineering development, however, lay in the Design Department, originally a section of the Drawing Office but afterward autonomous though ultimately responsible to first Crosby and then Goodman as Chief Engineer. When Goodman was promoted, J. D. ('Dennis') Usher, who had joined the department in 1948, became Chief Designer. He was a Cambridge engineer, not brilliantly imaginative perhaps, but of sound technical ability and quite imperturbable in a crisis. He was to hold the job for some thirty years. With him came H. C. ('Harry') Cooper, not so highly qualified as an engineer but of great imagination and a continual source of new ideas, who eventually became Managing Director of APV Kabushiki Kaisha, the group subsidiary in Tokyo.

With the need to increase productivity in the works, it had become steadily harder to get test plant and prototypes manufactured in the shops, so in 1950 it was decided to set up a development shop for the purpose. It was manned by the most advanced apprentices, who were thus able to get individual training.

The Staff Advisory Committee, founded in 1945, became an elected body in 1946. The most difficult subject it had to tackle was the annual staff profit sharing bonus. This had often provided a substantial proportion of total emoluments and fears arose as to whether company profits would be high enough to maintain payouts at that level. It was also becoming apparent that the scheme was not having the effect on staff morale that had been hoped and that, by tending to keep basic salaries down, it was making it hard to recruit and hold able young people, especially engineers and scientists for whom demand far exceeded supply.

A new and complicated scheme was agreed but it still did not prove wholly satisfactory and in 1951 the Board was considering linking the bonus directly to the rate of dividend on the ordinary shares.

When Seligman officially laid the foundation stone of the Crawley factory on 3 November 1951 (Illustration 16), it marked the end of an era for the company and the start of another.

The six years 1946 to 1951 had been crucial ones. Decisions to make the company public, to establish an overseas marketing net based on subsidiary companies and to build entirely new works and offices had been taken and largely achieved. This had been done while keeping the business not only going but expanding.

For all this the Board deserves full credit. They had set the shape of APV for many years to come. But there was a price to pay. The issued share capital of the company had increased from £56,000 to £1,385,000 with £650,000 loan stock. The Crawley buildings had yet to be put up. The seller's market that started in 1946 had practically disappeared by 1951 and supplies of raw materials had become very restricted.

In his Chairman's statement for 1951, Seligman, in reviewing future prospects, stated 'a considerable period of difficulty for your company must be envisaged.' He could hardly have realised how true that was to prove.

*Chapter 9*

# The Move to Crawley
# and its Aftermath
# 1952–1958

The next seven years were dominated by two events of fundamental importance to the company: the move to Crawley lasting until the end of 1955 and the financial crisis that followed it and involved a far-reaching reorganisation. Traumatic as the experience was for those who had to live through it, the result was greatly to improve the efficiency of the organisation and to fit it to expand in the years ahead.

The move itself went surprisingly well and caused far less dislocation than might have been expected. This was not only due to good planning of the buildings themselves and of the mechanics of the various transfers from London to Crawley, but because the management took great pains to keep employees and their families fully informed about all aspects of the move.

After a poor start, the building work went well so that the move into the new premises was able to begin in July 1952. The White City came first, then the machine shops and the press shop with part of the fitting and polishing shops from Point Pleasant.

By mid-December, the APV stage 1 move was finished. Five weeks later, the foundry move was complete and APV-Paramount, combining the operations of the APV foundries with Paramount Alloys, came into operation.

In the meantime, the plans for stage 2 were started but shortage of money forced delay so that it was not until May 1953 that the Board, having elected to raise more capital, could decide to proceed. This stage involved first completing the coppersmiths' fabrication shop alongside those already built. Auxiliary shops, office, research and development, and canteen blocks would follow. At this stage it was estimated that stage 2 would cost £715,000 of which roughly £500,000 would be raised as new capital and the balance provided by the sale of the Point Pleasant and Garratt Lane properties.

The foundations were being laid in September, by which time the estimate for the project had risen to £867,000. Not surprisingly, the Board considered halting the operation but, courageously, decided to proceed. Early in 1955 the fabrication shops were finished and the coppersmiths and remaining works office employees moved to Crawley. For the first time for fifteen years all APV production was housed in a single factory.

The final phase consisted of the new office, research and development, restaurant and garage blocks. These were occupied at the beginning of 1956.

All the company was now on one site. All, that is, except for the Chemical Engineering Department (CED). Webb had argued that it would not be possible for his department to carry on away from London. Until an appropriate alternative was found, the department would continue to operate at Northfields.

The transfer of a large and diffuse organisation to a completely new site had been accomplished extremely well but the demands on the firm's resources had been large. The effect on the employees was not negligible either. For many, Crawley had a curious feel of unreality and it was some time before they really settled down.

The overall business was running into difficulties, too, and at the worst possible time when the company's resources were strained to the limit. In the years immediately after the war, the sales of the company at home and abroad had expanded rapidly and profitably in a seller's market and supply, rather than price, had decided sales. By 1952 all this had changed. It was not so much a matter of sales volume; that remained at a little under £3 million for 1952 and 1953 and increased to an average of rather more than £3½ million for the four years 1954 to 1957[1]. It was the profitability of these sales which had fallen from about 18% overall in 1951 to less than a third of this in 1955.

To some extent this was due to internal factors, increased interest charges and higher overheads among them, but external ones, particularly the state of the market, were dominant. The general tightness of money all over the world began to be felt. Overseas markets introduced import quotas and licensing. It became harder to get customers to pay progress payments. Oddly enough, the raw material crisis, which loomed so large at the start of 1952 and which had attracted so much, largely wasted, R&D effort, did not develop.

Orders started to fall off early in 1952 as a result of a general business depression that only intensified as the year went on. As a result people were laid off in July. In an attempt to get more business, prices were lowered but by the end of the year the order input of normal company business had dropped very substantially compared with 1951, only offset by some Government orders of doubtful profitability. Export orders, too, had fallen to half their 1951 value. This was far too low to provide the sort of profit needed to justify the growing capital which had been increased during the year by the issue of 500,000, 6½% preference shares of £1.

The redundancies shook the confidence of the workforce. Productivity fell but by early 1953 the dairy industry world-wide was starting to look up. Orders increased steadily until, at the end of the year, the orders in hand were a record. As a result the workforce was expanded again.

This was a difficult year. The division between London and Crawley was at its worst and it was hardly surprising that the profit fell. The worst feature was the failure to improve deliveries or greatly to reduce work in progress under these conditions. The Board therefore decided to engage a Production Manager answering directly to the Managing Director independently of the

[1]For the group, the turnover, about £4¼ million in 1953, rose to some £6 million in 1955 and remained about at this figure until 1958.

Works Manager. In November E. R. ('Eddie') Cash was appointed. He came from the AEC Company (now part of British Leyland) at Southall where he had been Assistant Works Manager and where he had gained a knowledge of production engineering that was to prove of great value to the company. He personified the level-headed professional that Wilson had prophesied APV would need ten years before.

The following year orders improved substantially and included a large contract for Russia, worth £1 million. They remained at much the same level for the next four or five years. Profit also increased above the dangerously low figure for the previous year, but still was barely satisfactory. In spite of the new Production Manager, output was not going up as the Board wished. As a result it was decided to transfer Madron Seligman from APV-Paramount to the parent company as Works Director.

In 1955, the order intake again showed a tendency to fall and action was taken to tighten up financial control especially by improving overhead recovery which up to this time had been quite insufficient and even now remained far from complete. Departmental budgeting was introduced amid enormous grumbling. It is difficult now to realise that for forty-five years the company had operated not only without budgets but without any financial responsibility being laid on individual managers.

By now the overall effects of the move could be gauged. Crawley had centralised production on a site with space to expand but the substantial reduction in costs anticipated from the new equipment in a modern factory had not been achieved. On the contrary, except in the foundry, costs had continued to rise.

At the same time overheads were increasing and the Crawley bills kept coming in; they stood in the books at nearly £1.4 million[1] by the end of the year. One way or another the demand for money inside the company was growing. So, encouraged by an optimistic forecast of profit for the year, the Board decided in June to raise yet more capital. This consisted of a rights issue of ordinary 10s shares

[1]The total cost including plant was over £2 million.

150

in the ratio of 1 to 4 and £1½ million of debenture stock issued at 99%, intended to pay off the overdraft, other temporary loans and the loan stock. Together they yielded some £1.2 million of new capital.

But, in the upshot, while the sales were at a record level, just short of £4 million for the year, profit was very poor, only slightly better than 1953 and nearly 30% below that of the year before.

### Development and Licences

During all these difficult years, the main policy had been to try and get sufficient orders to provide enough productive hours to recover the overheads and service the capital as well as fill the new factory. The level of profits and means of reducing overheads seem to have taken a second place. It was natural therefore that management should look to new products and markets to produce new turnover. As a result, pressure came on the R&D staff to produce more new products, quicker and more economically.

There was a general belief that the company was lacking in new ideas. With hindsight that hardly bears examination; half a dozen of R&D's projects were still providing substantial business for the company twenty-five years later. It was, in fact, a very fruitful period technically.

It was certainly true, however, that the technical staff was called on to handle too many projects simultaneously so that it took longer than it should to bring them to completion. This was compounded by the time and money that was wasted on unsuccessful ideas licensed from outside. Finally, the pressure to get new products on to the market quickly led to their being sold before they had been fully tested in the field with disastrous results in at least two cases.

The Board and management were obsessed with the value of new products without fully counting the cost and were impatient to have them. Not least in this was Seligman who could not see why things should take so much longer than they had in the old days, thirty years before. His was still the dominant voice in the

Boardroom on technical matters although, even more than before, he was leaving financial matters to his colleagues.

Early in 1954 the Design Department was placed directly under Dummett's control. Thus was initiated a separate R&D department.

In June 1956, the Board, as part of a drive for greater turnover and seeking economies, decided on a review of the commercial prospects of the R&D work. A curb on R&D expenditure had to be envisaged.

It came quicker than was expected. Dummett was elected to the Board as Research Director in July. Almost at once he was required to cut back his staff and therefore his programme by some 10%. For the most part this could be done without too serious a loss.

In 1957, however, the department suffered much more gravely by the death of Reg Cuttell who had been transferred to it from dairy service work in 1953. His enthusiasm and vision were quite remarkable and APV owed a lot to his pioneer work on ultra high temperature heating and in-place cleaning.

Heat exchanger development centred on the production of further plates with the deep corrugated troughs devised for the heavy-duty HF but pressed from a single sheet of metal. It was not only for general industry and chemical duties that the demand was growing for higher throughputs, pressures and temperatures. All over the world smaller dairies and breweries were merging into large groups that operated in big centralised plants. New processes like ultra high temperature heating and the flash pasteurisation of beer were requiring operating temperatures of up to 140°C and pressures up to 7 atmospheres. It was therefore necessary to develop the gaskets, frames and auxiliaries to meet these new demands.

The first of this new generation of machines incorporating plates with deep corrugated troughs was termed the HX. It was introduced in 1953, is still widely used and is one of the most successful machines ever produced by the company. Though nowadays it would be rated as small, it was regarded then as a medium sized machine, for it was capable of pasteurising up to 1,000 gallons per hour of milk in a single unit. It was relatively robust and with excellent heat transfer characteristics.

The standard frame was stainless steel clad and can still be regarded as a handsome piece of plant.

It was followed by a whole series of frames and auxiliaries. This new range virtually replaced the HT except for very small duties.

The next plate in the new range to be developed was the HMB to replace the now practically obsolete HM, the first all-stainless steel plate introduced in 1946. This was virtually of the same design as the HX enlarged to twice the area and with larger ports to suit. It fitted the existing HM frame and was also launched in 1953.

The new HMB was capable of 3,300 gallons per hour pasteurisation duties often in conjunction with the HM panel and holder. It sold well and continued to do so. By the end of the decade practically all the original gunmetal HER machines, in dairies at least, had been replaced by these new machines.

By 1955 it had become clear that too much had been sacrificed technically in ensuring that the heavy duty HF was sufficiently robust and that most functions could be handled by a lighter but more efficient machine. A radical redesign was undertaken that led to a very similar plate but with gasket grooves pressed directly into the sheet. This new CHF as it was called virtually replaced its parent HF. It was introduced in 1957 and is chiefly remarkable for the fact that APV's first plates in titanium were pressed for it.

Botham was busy in the laboratory, in the works and with the rubber supply companies, working out and testing new gasket materials, particularly the new synthetic rubbers, to resist higher temperatures. This was a long, painstaking but essential piece of work carried out with his usual undemonstrative flair. By 1958, the company had a range of gaskets capable of meeting all the normal demands reasonably well.

Evaporation development was concentrated on the plate machine.

In a long series of tests the form of plate unit that was finally used in practice was gradually evolved (Fig. 6). Usher worked out the use of horizontal separators which, although now largely replaced by the more efficient vertical ones, helped in evolving layouts that were compact and easy to operate (Fig. 7). It was a taxing and costly development. At one time it even looked as if it ought to be jettisoned but, after a far-sighted plea from Webb, Seligman ruled that it should be pursued. This was his last decisive personal intervention in the detailed technical affairs of the company and a very valuable one.

At last the final form, consisting of a series of rubber gasketed evaporating plates, alternately rising and falling film, separated by steam heated plates and closed together in a frame like a plate heat exchanger, was evolved and patented in 1956. A prototype was run for some twelve months and eventually proved highly successful. It was shown at the Dairy Show in October 1957 and at the Achema in Frankfurt in 1958. It immediately started to sell and has been one of the company's major products world-wide ever since. Its compactness, flexibility and low hold-up left most of its competitors standing; only the falling film evaporators, that were also being developed just then, offered a real alternative in dairy, fruit juice and similar applications.

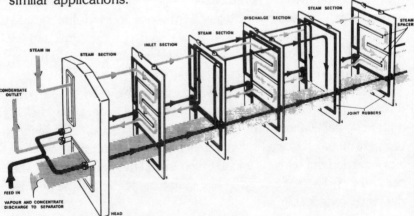

Fig. 6. Plate evaporator plates. Each unit consists of four plates. A complete effect consists of a number of such units clamped together in a frame.

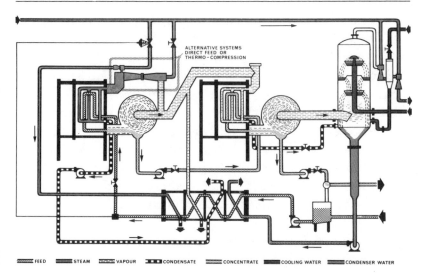

FEED ╏╏╏╏╏STEAM ═══VAPOUR ▪█▪CONDENSATE ▤▤▤CONCENTRATE ▬▬COOLING WATER ▨▨▨CONDENSER WATER

Fig. 7. Plate evaporator showing arrangement of a double effect vacuum plant with thermo recompression.

It is not too much to say that the plate evaporator transformed APV's approach to evaporation. Continual development had to go on to meet the innumerable problems that arose in extending its capabilities and efficiency but it was second only to the plate heat exchanger in the new markets that it opened up.

The HX heat exchanger made it possible to develop packaged plants for ultra high temperature heating and by the end of 1954 under Cuttell's enthusiastic leadership a point had been reached at which an indirect heated plant could be put on the market. Prototype tests had shown that it was possible to produce virtually sterile milk of good flavour but, in the absence of any method of sterile filling, the product had an insignificantly longer shelf life than pasteurised milk. The process was used as a pre-sterilisation step, greatly improving the effectiveness of traditional in-bottle sterilising lines, but for little else except in Japan.

The 'flash' pasteurisation, which in effect is sterilisation, of beer had been limited to dark, relatively lightly carbonated beers but with the HX and HMB it was possible to operate at pressures that

155

kept the carbon dioxide in solution at pasteurising temperatures so that the continuous pasteurisation of light ales and lagers became feasible.

Once more, the absence of a method of aseptic filling was of controlling importance. In Britain at this time most of the beer was dispensed from wooden cask or was sold pasteurised in bottles. The process was therefore relatively slow in finding application here. In Scandinavia, with its very high standards of filling hall hygiene, things were different. As a result, by mid-1955, out of twenty-nine HX pasteurisation plants ordered, twenty-two were for Scandinavia. This was the start of an important development.

Investigation of continuous brewing, another important brewery process, though not a highly successful one commercially as it turned out, was started at this time. In principle this involved treating the conventional brewhouse process as a series of chemical engineering operations and, based on this analysis, evolving the plant to handle them continuously.

The first step was wort boiling. As early as 1947, Seligman and Paine had conceived the idea of heating the wort to a much higher temperature and holding for a very short time thus achieving continuously, by analogy with HTST pasteurisation, the equivalent heat treatment to that obtained by boiling a batch for a couple of hours. Later a hop extraction step was added.

Pilot plant tests of this continuous wort boiling (CWB) were carried out at Northampton Brewery. After optimum operating conditions had been determined the company felt sure that it was on to a good thing, for the potential savings in energy, capital and space were enormous. It was not to be. When Northampton started to test market the CWB beer unblended with their normal brew, a number of their oldest pub customers started to complain of a 'nail varnish' aroma and taste. So vehement was this reaction that the tests were discontinued.

Nevertheless, it was agreed to continue with test marketing of the process and several plants were installed. In all cases something of the same reaction was found as at Northampton and it had to be withdrawn.

Then, early in 1957, APV was approached by the new Brewing Industry Research Foundation at Nutfield, who had evolved a small-scale continuous mashing process, to ask if the company would take part in joint development. R&D had already got some ideas as to how the process might go so the Board consented to go ahead and in the middle of the year it was agreed to examine both processes and to pursue whichever looked best.

David Shore, now Chief Process Engineer, was put in charge of the project. It looked most promising for, with many British breweries only getting a single brew a day out of their plant, the capital savings seemed likely to be large. The work was to occupy a lot of R&D's effort over the next few years.

While the simple two vessel cream treatment unit (CTU), developed a year or two earlier, was sufficient to meet Continental demands, Cuttell in 1952 and again in 1955 was involved in the Antipodes with far greater throughputs and removal of much more intractable flavours. The two vessel plants installed in New Zealand had to be modified and extended but it was not until early in 1953 when a mathematical analysis was done, leading to the 'series steam' process, that the CTU, virtually in its final form of three countercurrent spray columns in series, could be tested. First grade butter was made and the unit was now a saleable product thanks to Cuttell's energy.

A whole range of plants was developed to meet all required conditions and the units sold well, in the Antipodes and Europe particularly. The market was hardly big enough, however, to do much more than pay for the heavy development costs.

Subsequently, a demand arose for a still more efficient unit for very difficult creams and in 1956 Harry Cooper designed a multi-stage rotary disc column that was very effective and economic in steam but so fiendishly difficult to construct that it never really made money.

The ring joint (RJT) expanded stainless steel pipe fittings continued to sell well but were open to the criticism that they presented a somewhat unhygienic joint. Moreover, a number of competitors were marketing cheaper copies now that the design was a British Standard.

Late in 1953, Goodman patented the fitting which came to be known as the SP (semi-permanent). The joint was made by a tapered rubber bonded to a stainless steel ring that was locked between male and female spigots to make a completely crevice-free joint. It was expected to be especially suitable for lines cleaned in-place and the United States market.

The fittings were only to be made for expanding, and production of one comparable in price with the RJT proved difficult. It was two years or so before the fitting was ready for tests and then it was going to take further time to build up stocks to back a marketing campaign in America.

Matthews was insistent that he must have it to launch there in mid-1956. Accordingly, it was agreed to launch the product without long-term tests. It was a bad decision. Fittings were sold but it was found that in use, and sometimes even in storage, the bond between the stainless ring and the rubber gradually failed and the rubber fell out. The fittings had to be withdrawn and a new method of bonding evolved. Eventually it was found that a simple rubber ring could replace the composite one and so solve the difficulties.

The SP fitting was, however, the forerunner of the international standard ISS and IDF (International Dairy Federation) fittings and thus in the long run contributed much to the company's business in this field.

The original stainless steel 'Series V' cock had been heavy, expensive to produce and liable to jam, especially with hot liquids. These disadvantages were largely overcome by the WA (Wide Angle) cock, devised by Harry Cooper in 1956, a first-rate design which at once became the standard product and has remained so.

The APV stainless steel pumps then in use could be criticised for the unsanitary glands used to seal the shafts. A new range of stainless steel-clad pumps was put out at the end of 1953 incorporating a simple rotary seal to replace the gland. The redesign was done in a hurry and an ever-increasing number of the new seals gave trouble in the field. Eventually, two years later, the trouble was solved. Since then, the APV stainless steel pumps have proved a highly successful product.

At about this time the old practice of dismantling plants for cleaning every day began to be called in question. Botham evolved cleansers and circulation procedures for heat exchangers that were widely used but it was Cuttell who clearly saw the implications. In the last year of his life, he and Harry Cooper designed a spray ball for use in tank cleaning and demonstrated that this could give more reliable bacteriological results than hand cleaning. The way was opened for modern automated processes.

An important advance was made in the construction of brewery vessels. Until 1957, all fermenting vessels were cooled by circulating water through tubes suspended in a grid in the vessel. These were costly to produce, awkward to clean and rather unhygienic. A method was devised and patented of cooling through the wall of the vessel that not only eliminated these objections and was particularly suited to stainless steel construction, but actually strengthened the vessel itself. This 'external attemporation' at once replaced the old grid cooler and has been used, in one form or another, ever since. It gave a new fillip to APV's brewery fermenter business that was badly needed. Introduced in 1957, forty vessels had been installed by the end of that year.

None of this would have been as effective, perhaps even possible, without the developments in welding technique that were being pursued by Lancaster who, by now, had made a wide reputation as a welding specialist.

Aircomatic welding was introduced towards the end of 1952 from the United States and APV was the first firm in this country to apply it to the welding of aluminium. It had great advantages in speed and ease of welding over other methods available at the time and this was accentuated when an automatic version, the 'automatic Argonaut' was introduced a few years later. Heavy handling equipment was installed in the new shop at Crawley and also automatic submerged arc welding. Together these permitted the production of larger and heavier welded structures than ever before in the company.

An interesting process development was carried out by David Shore. In the early 1950s, open heart and lung surgery was just getting into its stride. Charles Drew, the chief cardiac surgeon at the Westminster Hospital, conceived the idea of applying profound hypothermia in such cases. If the patient's blood is cooled down steadily to below 28°C the heart stops beating. If the body is cooled further to about 15°C, the blood can be drained from the heart and, at this temperature, deterioration reactions in the body, particularly in the brain, are so retarded that there is a period of some two hours before any noticeable change takes place (as compared with seven minutes at normal blood temperature). During this time the operation can be done on a dry heart. The patient is then refilled with blood and warming up started. When the temperature reaches 28°C, the heart starts beating again and at 36°C the operation is complete.

In 1956, Drew asked Professor Saunders, under whom Shore had worked at Imperial College, for a recommendation and he had given the names of Shore and APV to collaborate in designing the necessary heat exchanger and controls. Shore threw himself into the project with great enthusiasm. The heat exchanger had to meet a very complex and difficult specification but a prototype was produced in the development shop and experimental work started at the hospital, at first on small animals, then large ones and eventually adult patients. All this was out of working hours and demanded considerable mental, as well as physical stamina. But eventually it was brought to a completely successful conclusion technically and a commercial unit sold.

It was not, however, the sort of product that APV was set up to market. Several were installed and many lives were saved with them but, generally, the medical profession opted for the more familiar heart and lung machine and the operation was never as successful as at one time it looked likely to be.

It is much to the APV Board's credit that, at a very difficult time, they were prepared to back such highly speculative work that could never bring in much financial reward.

In their frantic search for new products to bring in increased turnover the Board in 1953 took the decision to license products and know-how from outside, opining that 'the purchase of such items suitable for our manufacture could possibly always be desirable.' The experience of the next few years was to show how wrong this was.

The first of these licensed products was the Cooper range of stainless steel valves, a perfectly sound article technically, which was sold for a time quite well but eventually failed because the company was not in a position to market this class of product successfully in a highly competitive situation.

In 1953 several other agreements were signed. Much the most important was with the Manton-Gaulin Manufacturing Company of Boston, Massachusetts, to manufacture and sell their homogenisers. The Weir homogeniser had proved unsatisfactory. Matthews, however, was determined to have a good machine for he anticipated a large increase in sales of homogenised milk as had occurred years before in the United States. In this, as it happened, he was wrong but the agreement was a great success. The machine was first-rate; its manufacture brought new work to the Crawley shops and, years later, the Gaulin Corporation, as it now is, joined the APV group.

As APV got deeper into the supply of milk product plants, the need for a spray dryer became apparent. It was clearly not a project for APV to develop so a licence was sought for a suitable one for APV to manufacture. A number were investigated and eventually the choice fell on Karl Fischer of Berlin. Almost immediately a dryer in aluminium was sold to Lavenca in Venezuela. There was a stupid muddle over it. The plant did not work in consequence and although in the end it operated perfectly well, it was the last Fischer dryer APV installed.

Several members of the Board were convinced that the company should move into high-grade mechanical engineering, ignoring the fact that APV was basically a chemical engineering concern (that it applied its skills largely in dairies and breweries was irrelevant) and not a mechanical engineering one. More than that, the company had no real knowledge of the markets for such products. As a result much effort and money were wasted on trying unsuccessfully to develop products as diverse as mechanical ice-cream and ice-lolly freezers, beer fillers and churn handling plant.

The Rosenblad spiral heat exchanger, that was used to such good purpose in Scandinavian wood pulp plants, was licensed by the company in 1957 from Rosenblads Patenter in Sweden. This was a first-class machine but the manufacture was rather complicated and it took some time to get into its stride, not least because the sales force had difficulty in handling it and the plate machines together for, wrongly, they looked on them as basically competitive.

Altogether, the results of the plethora of licences taken during these years could hardly be called successful. But certain principles for licensing emerged and were accepted. By disregarding these, a lot of money had been needlessly lost.

## Sales and Marketing

In its search for new turnover, management looked for new fields of activity as well as new products.

It was the time of the early developments in atomic energy. Harwell's research work was at its peak; the first atomic power station was going to work at Calder Hall and at Dounreay development of the breeder reactor was just starting. Opposition from the environmentalists had not yet emerged and the possibilities, technical and commercial, seemed infinite. Companies

16. Richard Seligman laying the foundation stone of
the Crawley factory, 3 November 1951.

17. (Above left) Will Jenkins, Chairman of The A.P.V. Compa Limited 1958 to 1965.

18. (Above right) Peter Benson Managing Director of The A.P. Company Limited 1961 to 1974; Deputy Chairman 1974 to 1977; Chairman from 1977.

19. (Left) Ted Whitlock and Mrs Whitlock receiving a presentatio his retirement in 1955.

*Facing page:*
20. (Above) An all-stainless milk pasteurisation plant for Express Dairy Co. at South Morden (19 The processing units are HMB panel plants.

21. (Below) Welding an aluminiu atomic energy research reactor (1956), a fabrication job demand extreme accuracy.

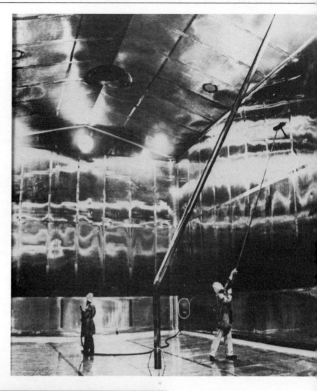

22. Stainless steel fermenting vessel at Guinness' Dublin brewery (1959). With a capacity of over 8000 barrels this is still the largest brewery fermenter in the world.

23. Continuous pure benzole products distillation plant at Llanwern, Gwent (1962).

everywhere were looking for opportunities to enter this enticing field, quite undeterred by the fact that money was being lost on almost every contract as a result of unfamiliarity with a new technology combined with wildly uncommercial competition.

APV, too, was seeking its niche. Liquid metals development looked promising but never paid off. The company was more successful in the fabrication of research reactor cores (Illustration 21). These were extremely difficult to manufacture, demanding standards of accuracy hitherto not achieved in large welded structures in aluminium. A number were made, both for home and overseas. If they were not very rewarding financially, these contracts gained the firm an excellent reputation in this field.

There were others but in fact none of these new market areas, except ice-cream, provided any permanent business for the company. It would have been better to have concentrated on its normal markets and not to have sought extra turnover almost wherever it was available.

The dairy department, whose turnover dominated the company's business, continued to supply a number of complete town's dairies all over the world based on the new heat exchangers (Illustration 20). But in 1953 they broke new ground by supplying a plant to Venezuela for the production of spray milk powder, cheese and butter. As well as the Fischer dryer it included a natural circulation evaporator, one of a number supplied during these years. It was the plate evaporator, however, that really enabled APV to break into the milk products market. Six plants had been sold by mid-1958, less than a year after it was put on the market.

A useful entry to the ice-cream industry was made by the supply of an ice-cream mix pasteurisation unit, the first in the country and the basis for official approval of the HTST process for it. This was followed in 1958 by a much larger unit that was one of the first to include in-place cleaning and central control of ingredients and their mixing, a pretty simple installation on present-day standards perhaps, but a forerunner of what was to come.

Everything at this time, however, was overshadowed by the big Russian contract, mainly for pasteurisation plants. It was worth over £1 million and was taken after long negotiations in Moscow in mid-1954. It lasted a year or so in the shops. The contract went well and the Russian Government proved a model customer but, nevertheless, such an enormous single order dislocated both the production and the marketing operations of the company. There were those who thought the company would have been better without it.

Under Eric Watson the brewery sales effort became better controlled although it was still not considered adequate. There remained a number of large fabrication contracts that had been taken at low profit margins and even some large development jobs on sale or return that had to be withdrawn.

Aluminium was still being used as well as copper and stainless steel for brewery vessels. In 1954, Guinness, Dublin, approached the company to design for them a series of transportable beer tanks that could be handled by forklift truck and that would nest together for transport by ship to Liverpool. The first batch of 100 was made in aluminium-magnesium alloy using the experience gained with aircraft tanks during the war, though later they were fabricated in stainless steel. A lot of other vessels were made for Guinness in Dublin at this time, notably a batch of twenty-one large aluminium storage vats and another batch of stainless steel 1,600-barrel closed fermenting vessels in which the new welding techniques were applied. These large vessels were dwarfed by a 3,250-barrel stainless steel fermenter, the largest in the world at that time, installed at the end of 1957.

The Chemical Engineering Department's (CED) main work continued in the alcohol and tar products field, although the power alcohol business was gone not to return for some thirty years.

As usual with a department of this kind, relying for most of its turnover on a few large turnkey contracts, business fluctuated considerably. In 1953, orders were below those for the year before but in 1954 they were a record for the department. They included substantial alcohol and yeast plants, and a large and advanced continuous tar acids plant for the North Thames Gas Board at Beckton.[1]

Amongst other contracts there were still one or two varnish plants, mostly extensions. Some effort was made to enter the synthetic resin field through the sale of reaction vessels but, early in 1959, this came to an end and with it APV's participation in the paint and varnish industry in which they had once been leaders.

Up to the end of 1955, CED had handled fabrication and standard plant sales to their industry as well as their main contracts. But from the beginning of 1956 when the Wandsworth staff finally moved to Crawley, leaving CED behind, a new Industrial Engineering Department (IED) at Crawley under Bill Jones took them over. This left CED as an autonomous division to concentrate on complete plants and contracting work generally.

There were several noteworthy fabrication contracts. In 1956, an order was taken for the design and manufacture of some huge aluminium reactor towers and distillation columns for a big hydrogen peroxide plant. One of them was the largest aluminium vessel to have been manufactured in this country.

Two other aluminium jobs were important. Four atomic reactor tanks were made, the last, in 1957, involving welding metal six inches thick. Then, at the end of that year, an order was taken for a huge insulated aluminium storage tank, the largest in the country, to hold imported LNG (liquified natural gas) at the experimental terminal being set up by the North Thames Gas Board on Canvey Island.

The major part of the Food Department's turnover was for fruit juice plant, mainly for de-aeration and pasteurisation units for export.

The natural circulation evaporators were not much of a success in this field; the hold-up was too long to give a good product. The prototype plate evaporator, however, was tested successfully for apple juice in 1957 and, in the next year, it was despatched for tests

[1]A model of this plant was presented to the Science Museum in 1956.

on citrus juices in Jamaica. This was the start of a most successful development.

Transport tank business did not go well. Competition was fierce, it proved impossible to realise prices that would give adequate profit, so it was decided to suspend production from the end of 1957 and only return to the market if redesign could reduce costs sufficiently. This, in fact, was done after a year of investigation. It only lasted a short time, however, before it was finally dropped, this time for good.

The foundry's performance was equally erratic. In June 1952, APV-Paramount Ltd had been created by merging Paramount Alloys at Slough with the APV foundries at Wandsworth and moving them together into their new premises at Crawley. Even then, it was proving hard to get an adequate order book for the non-ferrous side and, in 1953, a substantial loss was made partly due to lack of orders but also to a change in management. Len Smith had gone and Keeble had taken over under Madron Seligman. The following year, largely owing to the increased orders from the main works required by the Russian contract, a reasonable profit was made. By mid-1955 the foundry was coming to the end of its orders and facing layoffs, but now rescue was at hand.

At the end of the previous year, Keeble had left and been replaced as Deputy Managing Director by J. F. B. ('John') Jackson, a bluff North Country man of incisive mind and unlimited energy, who knew the foundry business through and through and, moreover, knew exactly what he wanted and how to get it. He saw clearly what was wrong with APV-Paramount. He recommended shutting down the unprofitable non-ferrous foundry, concentrating on the production of high alloy steel castings, marketing them wherever possible outside the company as well as inside it, and investing in the plant and methods needed to carry this programme through. To his great credit, Seligman agreed to back him even though it went against the grain to shut down the non-ferrous foundry with which he had been so deeply associated.

166

Not surprisingly, losses were made in this year and the next for it was a time of reorganisation, transition and expansion. The number of alloys produced was increased, new furnaces installed, the use of shell-moulding developed and external markets tapped.

By 1957, however, 'break-even' had been reached and Jackson could claim that APV-Paramount was 'the largest of British stainless steel foundries in operation' with an impressive number of developments in founding technique and in alloys melted.

In the following year, Paramount made a good profit. The change in its fortunes was entirely due to the vision of one man who was able to marry a perception of market needs to the technical resources available. To Seligman and the Board belongs the credit of having given him a free hand.

There was a general tendency to tighten up the organisation which had certainly got rather lax in the years immediately after the war. A new Sales Division was formed under Jack Matthews as Sales Director at the beginning of 1957. Bill Jones was to act as his deputy and remain Manager of the Industrial Engineering Department (IED). The Export Department under Dick Odgers became responsible for the executive handling of all overseas business. Brissenden and Watson remained in charge of dairy and brewery sales respectively, but the Food Plant Department was disbanded and its work distributed among the other three (the General Sales and Transport Tank Departments had previously been absorbed into IED).

This and other redeployment of staff were all put into operation within a month or two. It would have been too much to expect that it would all go equally well. Odgers, who had been appointed Export Manager in mid-1953 when Savory finally signed off, never settled down to the new arrangements and left in the middle of 1957 to be replaced by Bill Blois Johnson, a man of singular charm and indefatigable optimism.

Earlier, at the beginning of 1952, Jock Menzies had been appointed Sales Manager (home) of the Dairy Engineering

Department. It was not really a job that suited his highly individualistic methods even though it was restricted to sales matters outside the office and the supervision of outside sales staff. It was not, therefore, surprising when, at the beginning of 1954, Brissenden became Assistant Manager and deputy to Jack Matthews.

The sales of spares, fittings and other small items had increased enormously and, moreover, needed a different sales approach and method of handling to other products. In 1954 this was recognised by setting up a separate spares and fittings service.

During 1952, export business was gravely restrained by the difficulty in getting import licences in some of APV's main markets. As a result the orders received that year were less than half those taken in the previous year. In the following year things improved and then still further in 1954 when the order intake was double that in 1953. That year the export turnover was 31% of the total and the company was selling in sixty-one countries. 1955 was much the same but from then on increased import restrictions and intensified competition reduced the order intake and turnover but, more especially, the profitability. This was exacerbated by losses in some of the overseas subsidiaries. Moreover, a drive in 1957 to reduce stocks in the overseas companies had the effect of reducing their orders on Crawley.

It had long been felt that sales in Ireland, where the commercial atmosphere had completely changed after the war, should go through an Irish company. In 1954 discussions were started with Booth Brothers of Dublin on a possible joint venture. A new company, A.P.V. (Ireland) Ltd, was set up and a factory built at Drimnagh, near Dublin.

The new company did reasonably well in its first year, but towards the end of the following one negotiations had started with United Dairies on a possible merger between the Irish branch of their subsidiary, the Dairy Supply Company (Desco) and APV (Ireland). Desco was to take a 50% share in a new A.P.V.–Desco

(Ireland) Ltd. The merger became operative from the start of 1957 with Basil Booth of Booth Brothers as Managing Director.

In France, conditions were very difficult. The French Government was the first to impose import restrictions in 1952 – and the last to set up administrative machinery to distinguish essential from non-essential goods. This continued off and on through the following years with consequent fluctuations in profitability.

By 1952, APV had been virtually without representation in Germany for over fifteen years. Then Holstein und Kappert approached the company. They paid in full the royalties due from the manufacture of plates during the war and after it and proposed negotiating a new agreement. It was a shrewd move on their part. Plock, their new Managing Director, saw clearly that what his company needed was a new stainless steel plate heat exchanger and that to produce their own would be a long and dubious project. An agreement was reached and so was renewed an association that, not without its ups and downs, has survived in some form or another to the present time.

In Holland, the difficulties with Merkens continued. A dairy engineer was appointed as technical representative and it was agreed that sales should be managed from Britain with Merkens operating on a commission basis. Then, in 1955, 'old' Merkens died. APV owed much to its first agent, even if his last few years had been clouded by illness and strife. The way was now clear to establish a Dutch subsidiary company, but it was to be another ten years before this came about.

In Sweden, Bröderne Herrmann, APV's brewery agents, were persuaded to set up a dairy department in 1952. APV Nordiska was wound up two years later, the Stockholm office was closed in 1956 and the ill-starred Swedish venture was finished.

In the USA the split from York led to far-reaching developments. In 1952, it was decided to set up a dairy division under Jock Menzies' son, Alister, who joined APV shortly after the war, and to rename the company A.P.V. Company Incorporated. At the start of

1957 Earl Hall retired but remained as consultant while Menzies became President.

Sales increased steadily though profits remained small but by 1958 the corner was turned and the new company was now set for profitable development.

In Canada things did not go nearly so well. Early in 1955, Wallace suggested that APV should acquire Walker-Wallace in Toronto. A new company A.P.V. (Canada) Equipment Ltd was formed with all shares held by APV. At the end of the year Pickard left India to become President in Canada and Wallace then became Chairman. He died early in 1958.

At this stage, everyone, including Pickard and the Board, underestimated the problems of operating in Canada, one of the most difficult markets in the world. It was decided to manufacture large vessels. As this would not have been possible at Toronto, Pickard recommended acquiring a factory of nearly 50,000 square feet in Newmarket, some thirty miles north. The purchase was negotiated in July 1956. This involved getting rid of the Toronto premises but they proved hard to dispose of. As a result the company had to infuse further capital when it could least afford it.

The whole operation proved a disaster. It was not possible to get sufficient work to fill Newmarket and there were serious labour troubles. The Canadian company lost heavily in 1957. In the meantime, Pickard had agreed to return to Crawley and had been replaced but the new man did not prove able to stop the rot and a similar loss was made in the following year.

In August 1958, the Board was forced to the decision to sell off Newmarket as best they could, transform APV (Canada) into a purely sales operation and acquire suitable premises in Toronto. Later in the year a further infusion of capital was needed and the factory was finally disposed of, at a loss, in 1960.

Brazil, too, gave cause for anxiety. The Board had agreed in 1951 that further temporary working capital should be provided. A major difficulty was inflation and high internal prices that devalued the cruzeiro and made the remittance of sterling virtually impossible. In Brazil itself, however, sales were going well and the subsidiary's operation was extended to cover the brewing industry with remarkable success.

Early in 1953 it had become clear that the commercial management of APV do Brasil had been extremely lax. As a result Felsberg resigned and Robinson was appointed Technical Director under Oscar Landmann as Managing Director.

The subsidiary struggled on for the next two years. The Board even considered the possibility of withdrawing from Brazil altogether but fortunately more farsighted, or at least more courageous, counsels prevailed. It was decided instead to extend the fabrication work.

At the end of 1955, APV do Brasil moved to new and larger premises with greater scope for work of this kind. From then on the fortunes of the company improved, even though there were still currency and economic problems and periodic injections of further working capital were needed.

Pickard took over from Len Smith in Calcutta early in 1952. Under his leadership, the company began to pick up and ran profitably with increasing turnover on a widened scope of activity. As a result some of the debt was eliminated, the freehold of the Dum-Dum land acquired and the offices moved there a year or two later.

APVEC's business was almost entirely internal, however, and because of strict currency control involved practically no import of plant from Britain. So, in spite of continuing profitable operation, the Board began to look for means of reducing the financial commitment in India. In May 1955 it was decided to seek Indian interests who would take up 49% of the capital and also find an Indian as successor to Pickard.

Then, towards the end of the year, Pickard left for Canada. He was succeeded, not by an Indian, but by J. G. ('Jack') Brown from Wandsworth. He was appointed for a probationary period of six months and stayed for fifteen years.

171

In 1956, both turnover and profitability grew and efforts to obtain an infusion of Indian capital increased. Then, in the following year, trading grew more difficult, Indian taxation became more onerous and profit was reduced. As a result it was not to prove possible to float a public company until 1964.

An important new market, and one destined to become of great interest, was Japan. There, the small additional shelf life obtained from the ultra high temperature treatment of milk in the new large town's dairies proved commercially attractive. As early as 1955 several plants were despatched but it was to be several years before proper marketing arrangements were set up there.

The new Australian subsidiary struck difficulties almost at once for in February 1952 the Government announced import cuts that caused immediate cessation of shipments from Britain. Cash became very tight and some increase of working capital was required. Then restrictions were relaxed and business improved only to be halted again by reimposition of import control. So it continued with fluctuating turnover and profits through the period.

### The Crawley Operation, Crisis and Recovery

At Crawley, the pressures on works management were considerable. Much was expected from the appointment of Eddie Cash as Production Manager but the split between works and production management led to divided loyalties. The appointment of Madron Seligman as Works Director at the beginning of 1955 was intended to rectify this.

There was continual pressure for greater productivity and, in fact, something was achieved. The ratio of sales invoiced to productive wages and bonus rose from 6.6 in 1951 to 8.5 in 1953 but owing to substantial increases in wage rates as a result of national awards fell back to 6.8 in 1955.

The company had looked to complex and comparatively heavy fabrication as a source of new and increased turnover. To meet this a lot of new and costly equipment was put down in the new Crawley shop that by 1954 was employing about 50% more coppersmiths than the firm had ever employed before the war.

Following several years of niggling negotiations on wage rates and bonuses, labour relations reached their nadir in the spring of 1956 when the works came out on strike for three weeks. It seriously affected the year's output. It was the first strike of any size in the history of the company and was a bitter blow to Seligman.

Ostensibly, at least, the reason for the strike was the redundancy of several operatives. The Board took the view that there must be no reinstatement of those laid off as part of a settlement. However, in unofficial negotiations May had committed the company to take back one of the men made redundant if there was a suitable vacancy. The strike was settled. A vacancy did arise but the man involved refused it as he felt he was not qualified to do it.

Following the strike and the settlement against Board instructions, Madron Seligman was asked to prepare a plan for unifying the works management.

Eventually, in June 1957, it was decided that Pickard was to be brought back from Canada and made Works Director. A month or two later, May relinquished his post as General Works Manager and was succeeded by Cash who was given responsibility for both works and production. Pickard took up his new post in March 1958 and May retired in October.

Ted Whitlock had retired from the Board some time before in July 1955 (Illustration 19). His going, coinciding as it did with the winding up of the Wandsworth phase of the firm, marked the end of an era. He had joined APV in June 1910 and had given outstanding service as coppersmith, Foreman, Works Manager and Director.

Through 1956 management was struggling to maintain sales which, in the event, did not reach the budgeted level. This was against a background of low profitability, unrecovered overheads and excessive inventory, leading to big loans and high interest charges. As a result the return on capital employed had dropped from 17 % to 4½ %.

This was the situation when, in June 1956, Baigent reviewed the 1955 accounts for the Board. He pointed out that, while the gross profit had improved over the previous year, this had been more than eliminated by an increase in factory and general overhead expenses. Off-setting this to some extent there was a sum brought into the accounts for taxation provisions, taken in previous years and no longer needed, a once-for-all bonus. It was only this that would permit paying a 10% dividend without raiding other reserves to do so.

The extra £1.2 million of capital employed as a result of the share and debenture issues had virtually all become locked up in additional fixed assets, largely at Crawley; also payments to subsidiaries, mainly in Canada and APV-Paramount, combined with further increases in current assets, almost all in larger stocks and work in progress.

'Was a dividend to be paid?' he asked. The Board decided it should be. In this they were reinforced by a conviction that major reductions in overheads were to be made. They were perhaps also influenced by consideration of the effect on the shareholders that passing the dividend would have so soon after raising substantial extra capital.

When the Board met after the Annual General Meeting in July, the position was reviewed. It was agreed that investment in inventory must be reduced if capital was to be available for the subsidiary companies, for no more would be available from the market; that debtors must be reduced and customers' progress payments increased; and that research and development expenditure be controlled. It was the mixture as before especially as, at the same time, it was reported that overhead recovery for 1956 was being budgeted at £100,000 below expenditure. The only definite action was a restriction of R&D projects with resultant reduction in staff that was hoped to save about 20% of the budgeted R&D expenditure.

The following day Baigent and A. C. Furse-Roberts, recently appointed Company Secretary, visited Seligman Brothers who wished to reduce their revolving credit to APV as soon as possible, ostensibly because of the credit squeeze then operating. The APV representatives replied that any prompt repayment would cause severe difficulties and suggested that consideration be deferred until May 1957.

In the meantime the Stock Exchange had reacted badly to the 1955 results and Chairman's statement, and the share price was falling.

Then the crunch came. In the middle of August, Peter Seligman was asked to meet Seligman Brothers. After reiterating their criticism of the company's performance and financial direction, it was disclosed that Seligman Brothers were negotiating a merger with another Merchant Bank (later revealed to be S. G. Warburg & Co.). In the course of these negotiations, Seligman's loan to APV had been discussed and their associates had declined to take on the company's credit line. This left APV in the unenviable position of either having to pay off the loan at once or cause breakdown of the merger.

There was, however, a way out, Seligman Brothers indicated. If a leading accountant were to make an appraisal of the company's structure and performance, and report favourably, their associates might well reverse their decision.

At this point Peter Seligman showed his mettle. He must have realised that a survey of this kind could involve unpleasant consequences for members of his family and his associates but he saw, too, that it would be to the benefit of the company and so he agreed to it without demur. In doing so, he was not without criticism from some members of the Board who feared a sell out to 'big business'. It was a wise decision though one, however, in which the Chairman played little part.

J. T. ('John') Corbett of Peat, Marwick, Mitchell and Company was suggested and accepted as the investigator. He was a chartered accountant of great distinction with a wide knowledge of industry and a thoroughly human and approachable character, just the man for the job.

He started work almost at once and very soon was putting forward his main criticisms: the level of inventory, the method of valuation of it, especially the practice of taking overhead recovery on stock orders, and the rate of depreciation of slow-moving stock. He pointed out that these might have involved the payment of excessive tax. There were also other points of difference including the 'sales reserves' and the amount of profit taken on them.

The interim dividends were now due; the preference were paid but not the ordinary. By now, rumours were rife in the works; ICI or the Prudential were taking over, the banks were foreclosing and so on. They were dealt with by personal statement. Strangely enough there was no other strong reaction.

Eventually a revaluation of the stocks and current work in progress was made. Against the consequent write-downs a tax rebate amounting to about 40% of them could be claimed leaving a net amount that could be provided from revenue reserves without any need to dip into capital.

At the same time, Corbett was able to write reassuringly to Frank Keighley, General Manager of the company's bankers. Presumably he also gave some reassurance to Warburg's for in October Seligman Brothers were again granting credit.

By now, however, the ordinary shares had fallen to 7s (35p) and confidence both inside and outside the company badly needed restoring. Corbett was accepted as consultant to the Board. From then on, for nearly twenty years, his wise opinion was available to the company.

It had been clear from the beginning that the investigation could not be limited to purely financial matters. Certainly the financial direction had been called in question by the investigation and would have to be strengthened as would the general administration. The divided works management needed clearing up. By setting up a single sales division, the chain of administration would be greatly simplified.

As early as November, the name of H. P. N. ('Peter') Benson was being canvassed as a first-class executive. In January 1957 he was appointed 'to take control of the financial organisation' of the group, elected in April to the Board and started at Crawley in May. It was a crucial appointment. As a first-class chartered accountant and administrator, fresh to the company, he was able to push through the sometimes unpleasant restrictive measures that the company needed to bring it back to profitable working, rather as Wilson had done in 1920. He also had had experience of the engineering industry as a result of some years spent with Mowlem and Company, the civil engineering contractors. More important, his bluff straightforwardness quickly gained him the respect and then the affection of work people and staff alike. At the end of 1957, Baigent retired on the grounds of ill health a year before his normal retirement date and Peter Benson became Finance Director. Shortly before, K.A. ('Ken') Grover had been appointed Company Secretary.

Leslie Davies also resigned and Gerald Seligman, who had given notice of his wish to retire before any question of the Corbett investigation had arisen, finally left in April 1957 after more than forty years' service.

Finally, in October 1956, Richard Seligman gave notice of his intention to relinquish the chairmanship as soon as a suitable successor was found. He was already seventy-eight and the Board, with regret, agreed that the time had properly arrived for him to retire. A number of possible candidates were reviewed but finally the choice fell on W. E. ('Will') Jenkins. The Board had been seeking a non-executive Chairman, versed in industrial management. Will Jenkins was exactly the man they were looking for. Shrewd, meticulous, he came from the Esso Petroleum Company where, as Managing Director, he had gained a very wide experience of industry in all its aspects. The very fact of a man of his reputation joining the Board would at once improve the standing of APV, in the City especially.

He was elected to the Board in May 1957 and, when Seligman relinquished the chair at the Annual General Meeting in June 1958, he succeeded to it. He proved an excellent choice and it was largely his wise guidance that brought the company out of a very difficult period and set it on the path of expansion it was to follow for the next twenty years.

The history of the years from 1956 to 1958 is quickly told. It was a period of recovery from the traumatic events of the autumn of 1956 although it was not without difficulties of its own.

In October 1956, the first budgets for 1957 were considered. The invoiced sales were estimated as unlikely to exceed £4 million. As it happens the estimate proved hopelessly optimistic but that made the reduction of overheads even more urgent. Cuts were already being made in research and development; the next for consideration were the works bonus and staff profit-sharing bonus.

Then it was agreed to aim to eliminate the bank overdraft and to make the subsidiaries self-supporting.

Early in 1957 Matthews, under pressure, produced a revised sales forecast for the year of more than £4 million, with what justification it is hard to say. While fabrication work was coming in fast, heat exchanger business was static and export orders had slumped: however, the orders began to come in better in the spring.

In May the interim preference dividends were paid. Benson and Jenkins immediately made their influence felt as the Board began to consider the 1956 accounts with all their revaluations and alterations.

Certainly there was not much comfort to be found in the figures. The sales for the company were down on the previous year although for the group they remained about the same. The group profit, however, was seriously down, amounting to only 4% on sales and 4½% on capital employed. As a result largely of Corbett's revaluation, the inventory was reduced substantially over that reported in the previous year's accounts. This was the one really bright spot in the accounts, for overdraft and loans had been practically eliminated as a result. The cost of the revaluation was met partly by the moneys from sale of the Wandsworth properties, and partly from the revenue reserves. The ordinary dividend was passed.

By the middle of 1957, the order intake was improving rapidly, mainly for dairy and IED. The overhead position was also better. The under-recovery, thanks to lower finance charges, was only slightly worse than budget.

In September the Board was concerned to learn that the Australian company, that had been estimated to show a modest profit at the half year, had in fact made a loss, half of which referred to the previous year. CED, too, had made a loss. The consolidated results at that point were very poor so the interim ordinary dividend was passed although those on the preference shares were paid.

Although the orders continued to come in well, they could not prevent the invoiced sales for 1957 being badly down. Not only that, but there were serious losses on a number of big brewery jobs as well as the Canadian expenses, so the pre-tax profit was again very low giving a return on capital of under 4½%. Total inventory was about the same as in 1956. Nevertheless, much better customer payments had been obtained so that the net work in progress figure had actually been reduced.

The budgets for 1958 were based on a forecast of £4 million invoiced sales, once more to be proved hopelessly optimistic but, this time, not so catastrophically so.

Early in the year recession was being felt in the USA and the major dominions. It was therefore necessary to revise the sales forecast. There was now no prospect of getting the budgeted overhead recovery so it became necessary to cut staff.

It had also been agreed that the company should concentrate on its standard products, reduce diversification that attracted costs that were hard to recover and reduce the overhead expenditure accordingly, mostly by staff redundancies in all departments.

The Board were anxious to avoid hardship and to spare long-service personnel, especially those with over twenty-five years' service but, nevertheless, several were involved and were given early retirement on special terms. Among these was Bill Paine who had joined APV as an apprentice forty-seven years before.

In spite of these measures and a reasonable profit for the first quarter, the prospect at mid-year did not look too good. Profit was falling and was expected to fall still further as fabrication work taken at poor margins came through. It also looked as though there was still going to be a substantial under-recovery of overheads in 1958.

So things did not look very bright when the Annual General Meeting was held on 11 June at Crawley. It was the last time Richard Seligman was to preside over a meeting of 'his' company and it was the nearest to an acrimonious one that had occurred in its history. Some pointed and, as usual on such occasions, a few unreasonable questions were asked and answered. Nevertheless, with only one shareholder abstaining, the accounts and directors' report and all other resolutions were passed. Then Seligman announced his retirement from the chair and was very prettily thanked by Hugh Goodman for the shareholders.

Later in the day the Board elected him Life President with the right to attend all Board meetings. This he did religiously; indeed he attended Crawley every day until literally that of his death. The Board also recorded 'its warm appreciation of his lifetime's service given to the company'.

This valediction and the myriad good wishes that showered in from all over the globe and everywhere in the company, did something to sweeten what for him must have been a bitter moment. He would no doubt have liked to hand over when the company was at its height and not when its future seemed in doubt and it had just had to lay off some of his oldest associates.

It was, indeed, the formal end of an epoch in the history of APV though in fact it had come to an end two years before. What neither Seligman nor anyone else could know, was that it was also a turning-point, that the worst was now over and that he had brought the company to a point where it was entering into a phase of continually increasing prosperity.

The previous two years had seen APV grow up. It had now ceased to be in any way a family concern and had become a fully-fledged public company albeit with strong and valuable traditions. That it had reached this stage from near-bankruptcy in such a short time was a typical example of the application of sound management and financial principles. That this came about was partly due to the beneficent action of the City institutions, anxious – no doubt not wholly altruistically – to save a potentially valuable company with the knowledge of what needed to be done and how to do it. Even more it was due to the character of the company's Managing Director; his loyalty to the company and all those associated with it; his open-mindedness in accepting unpalatable advice and his determination to put it into action. As a result, the Board had been greatly strengthened and now had the men of wide experience it had previously lacked to carry it forward into the future.

# Chapter 10
# Will Jenkins' Chairmanship
# 1958–1965

As soon as Jenkins took the chair, Richard Seligman became President. While he attended every Board meeting he made no attempt, quite properly, to influence policy. He did, however, address a dignified message of thanks to all members of APV through *The APV News'* first number.

At the beginning of 1959, Peter Benson became Deputy Managing Director. Then, at the start of 1961, Peter Seligman became Deputy Chairman and Joint Managing Director, in charge of sales and research and development, and Benson, Joint Managing Director responsible for production, purchasing, finance and administration. It is often maintained that having joint managing directors is a mistake and leads to unnecessary conflict with no one man responsible for decisions. In this case it worked remarkably well. The two Peters were complementary in character and training, realised the fact and respected each other's point of view. The friendly atmosphere between them spilled over into the Boardroom which, encouraged by Jenkins, became a very pleasant place to work in. Not that Board meetings under Richard Seligman's chairmanship had been unfriendly, but he had old-fashioned, not to say strict, ideas as to how such meetings should be conducted. Under him, laughter in the Boardroom was about as thinkable as in church.

The next years were ones of almost uninterrupted growth. During this time The A.P.V. Company Ltd and its subsidiaries became A.P.V. Holdings Limited, with the APV Company as the principal subsidiary in the group. At the time it occurred, the effect of the change was more organisational than actual. The day-to-day operation of the Board was but little changed, so it would be artificial to make an arbitrary division in this chronicle.[1]

The drama of the previous years was followed by a period of consolidation and expansion. It was not without its difficulties but the company, having survived its worst crisis, took them in its stride as a result of sensible leadership backed by the loyal support of workforce and staff.

The development of the company at this time demonstrates strikingly the effect of good, especially sound financial, management. Every Board meeting considered the overall financial position, turnover, profitability and overhead recovery against well established budgetary procedures, and took action accordingly.

As a result, Board proceedings were concerned more with financial performance and less with technicalities than they had been in the past. All this was based on the excellent financial information and analyses that Benson had organised and made available for the Board. They formed an essential part of his campaign to get the finances of the firm under control. They, and his insistence on prompt and effective management action on them which he kept largely under his personal direction, were crucial factors in bringing the company back to profitable operation.

Labour relations in the works, partly as a result of the move to Crawley and partly as a result of the new organisation, became steadily less patriarchal and rather stormier. National negotiations between the Engineering Employers' Federation and the unions were taking the place of local arrangements. Nevertheless, the 'family' feeling and tradition had by no means been lost. Both Jenkins and Benson recognised its value and did much to see that it was preserved.

For the previous twenty years the Board had been continually involved with the problems of premises and the financial difficulties

---

[1]The financial results quoted in this chapter are from the consolidated accounts of The A.P.V. Company Ltd to 1961, and for A.P.V. Holdings Ltd from 1962.

they brought with them. Now, comfortably settled at Crawley with growing profits, these no longer existed. Loans and overdrafts had become things of the past. Instead there arose the haunting spectre of take-over by a large organisation. To counter this the company had to expand – in its normal business by new products, or by taking over other companies itself.

A policy of acquisition therefore emerged for the first time. The Board did not follow one of acquisition for acquisition's sake as did so many of the conglomerates that were growing up at that time. If a firm was to be taken over then it must fit in with the technical or marketing expertise of the group. The take-over had to follow reasonable industrial logic.

Another result of the company finding itself with money in its pocket for the first time for many years, was increased investment in plant. Jenkins, shrewd and farsighted as he was, saw the necessity of increasing productivity in the shops. He instigated a policy of replacing old equipment with highly sophisticated automatic machines that made the machine shop one of the most advanced of its kind in the country. In Eddie Cash as Works Manager, the company had just the man to carry such a policy through. His knowledge of complex production engineering gained in the automobile industry, and an innate zeal for automated machinery alike, prompted him to follow it with enthusiasm.

Although already in 1957 the effects of reorganisation were being reflected in increased profitability, this was offset in the following years by a marked fall in sales in almost all markets at home and abroad as a result of a general recession. Competition was severe and prices were forced down in some cases to unremunerative levels. A number of staff redundancies followed and the load on the shops and foundries became light enough to affect morale and cause some restriction of effort. Nevertheless, with an output similar to 1957 (about £6 million) and in spite of heavy expenses in Canada, the group profit for 1958 was more than doubled and a modest dividend of 5% on the ordinary shares could be paid. These improved results were attributable mainly to the economies and improvements that had been effected throughout the organisation.

In 1959 sales improved with reduced production costs. It proved a good year for the parent company and all the overseas subsidiaries except Canada, so that with only a modest growth of invoiced sales to £6.4 million the profit again increased substantially and the dividend on the ordinary shares was brought up to 8½%. Better still, the cash position was so much better that substantial investment in new plant could be started, including large furnaces for APV-Paramount. The programme continued for several years.

In June 1960, the Golden Jubilee of the foundation of the company was suitably celebrated by junketings at Jordans, an Open Day at the works and a presentation to 'Doctor Dick' of an album containing the signatures of everyone in the company.

Unprofitable non-ferrous melting at APV-Paramount ceased and was replaced by further special steel furnaces. It was a successful move; the order intake for the year increased by a third over the previous one and the profit was a record. The foundry could now produce more than 250 tons of liquid steel a week and individual castings of five tons finished weight. It was now the largest and most modern plant of its kind in the country.

It was also a record year for the APV Company; sales reached over £4¾ million, having never previously exceeded £4 million. The group sales increased to £7.1 million yielding a profit up by more than 50% to over £¾ million. A dividend of 11¼% on the ordinary shares was paid. Production for the year was up by 16% at Crawley in spite of the introduction of a forty-two hour week.

Orders continued, nevertheless, to come in at a rate exceeding that of production and deliveries increased. The company accordingly adopted a selective sales policy concentrating on standard and high profitability lines.

Faced with this situation, the APV Company Executive Committee, set up a year or two previously to handle day-to-day operations, considered the possibility of setting up a production shop in the North of England. At this point, a small fabricating company in Blackpool, Stainless Steel Plant (SSP), came under consideration. Towards the end of the year APV acquired the whole of its issued share capital.

In October, it was decided to increase APV's issued share capital by £250,000 by creating 500,000 new ordinary 10s shares from the capital reserves, and allotting them to the existing shareholders in the ratio one to five.

Abroad, Canada, now reduced to a sales company, was just starting to be profitable and a Belgian subsidiary was being set up. This was associated with the creation of the European Economic Community, for it provided a sales base in Benelux. It was felt necessary to safeguard the company's position, as the consequences of Britain not entering the Common Market for APV's European business were feared to be much more serious than they in fact proved to be. On the other hand, the creation of the European Free Trade Area (EFTA) had provided competitors in Sweden and Denmark with a competitive advantage that they had previously lacked. This was bound to intensify competition in the UK. The Board, then as ever since, was firmly in favour of Britain joining the EEC, naturally enough for the Common Market countries accounted for about a quarter of the company's exports which now in all amounted to about half its total output.

The year 1961 had much the same pattern of increasing sales and profits, though there were some signs of a fall-off towards the end of it, particularly in some export markets. The total volume of exports declined, partly due to increased import duties but also because the Australian subsidiary was floated, as had always been intended, as a public company. APV lost financial control as a result, so that the turnover and profit could no longer be consolidated in the group accounts.

Nevertheless, the rest of the group, and particularly the parent company, did so well that the turnover for 1961 increased to £7.4 million (it would have been over £8 million with Australia) and the profit, largely as a result of excluding less profitable work, rose by 20%. This allowed an increase in the ordinary share dividend to

12½%. At the same time, large sums of money continued to be invested in new plant for the Crawley machine shop and for APV-Paramount who not only turned in a record profit but started a significant export business.

The high level of orders was, however, causing difficulties in the works. In spite of increased production and larger progress payments by customers, the net inventory continued to increase rather faster than sales.

The position was aggravated by the difficulty in recruiting skilled labour. The labour pool in Crawley was very restricted. Indeed, the company was losing men to other companies in the neighbourhood who were not so scrupulous about holding to wage agreements and extra productivity from the new machines could not compensate so that more and more work had to be subcontracted.

Stainless Steel Plant was now taking on a lot of Crawley's fabrication work. It therefore became necessary to extend the Blackpool production. This could not be done at the existing Cleveleys factory, which was in a residential area, because of the noise. A new site was acquired in Marton, a few miles away, at the end of the year and a new shop of 25,000 square feet with offices authorised.

Towards the middle of 1962 the pinch began to be felt. Growing inventory reduced liquidity. Sales of heat exchangers were falling. In November, the Board was beginning to look with a jaundiced eye on the capital expenditure for the following year, for the forward load on some parts of the factory was starting to lighten.

Nevertheless, 1962 did not prove as bad a year as was feared. The order intake for the APV Company kept up reasonably until the last quarter but the overseas subsidiaries did well so that, with greater output from the works, the sales increased to £8.3 million, although the profit was only slightly up. Again, a 12½% dividend was paid on the ordinary shares, though on an increased number for at the Annual General Meeting in May the authorised capital of the company had been increased to £2,900,000 by creating a further one million ordinary 10s shares. Of these, 600,000 were paid up by capitalising revenue reserves and distributed in the ratio of one to five as a bonus issue to the existing shareholders.

At this same meeting, an innocuous resolution changing the name of the company to A.P.V. Holdings Limited as from the beginning of 1962 was passed. This was the final step in a series of complex operations which left APV Holdings retaining the assets of all its subsidiary companies while The A.P.V. Company Ltd carried on the Crawley business as before as the holding company's chief subsidiary.

The holding company became reponsible for overall policy and financial control of the group and its members. The Board members were identical with those of the previous APV Company except that John Jackson, Managing Director of APV-Paramount, was elected to it, a fitting recognition of his brilliant technical and commercial achievement in transforming the foundry business.

The subsidiary companies became independently responsible for their own performance both commercially and technically.

The APV Company's operations were little affected immediately by the change. The Board remained virtually unaltered; it was not until Jenkins retired from the chair that it was substantially reorganised. However, as more companies, at home and abroad, came into the group the near-dominance of the APV Company was steadily eroded and it gradually became in fact what it had been for some time in theory, just one of several large subsidiary companies, *primus inter pares*, maybe, because its factory provided over two-thirds of group turnover, but not pre-eminent.

It had been found necessary to increase overhead recovery rates and this, combined with increases in material costs, was causing a reduction in profitability. At the same time, owing to a shortage of overtime working and lack of operatives, overheads were still not being recovered. In the middle of 1962 things looked better at Crawley as a result of some substantial orders, but a recession in the chemical industry was affecting the Industrial Engineering Department and SSP whose new factory was nearing completion. This meant relinquishing the lease on the old rented premises at

Cleveleys. Cash, now on the APV Company Board, proposed that they should be turned into a machine shop. This would be an extension of the Crawley shop and would only be kept at Cleveleys until there was accommodation available at Marton. It is still in operation.

Under-recovery of overheads continued and was exacerbated by national wage and salary awards. There were some large losses to be accommodated, too. These, and the poorer results from several subsidiaries, resulted in a merely modest increase in profit for the year.

The temporary decline in the fortunes of APV continued into the following year which was the only one in the twenty years to 1977 to see a fall in turnover and profit for the group as compared with the previous one, although the fall was in no way catastrophic. Considering the severe recession in the capital goods industries at the end of 1962 the result – sales £½ million down at £7.8 million and profit reduced to £858,000 – was satisfactory. The ordinary dividend was increased to 15% with ample cover.

In his Chairman's statement, Jenkins was able to point out that despite several increases in costs of materials, wages, salaries and services, prices had only gone up 10% over the five years 1959 to 1963 while overhead expenses had increased 44% over the same period. Modern machinery and methods combined with all round efficiency had enabled the company to contain these increases and still produce good results.

The policy of the Board had been to retain rather over two-thirds of the profit after tax to provide for expansion at Crawley and in the subsidiary companies. In the five years, about £2 million of profits, plus depreciation, had been ploughed back of which £1¼ million was for new plant and equipment, the new Blackpool factory and new companies overseas. The rest provided working capital to finance increased turnover.

The comparatively poor results in 1963 were really a result of the low order intake in the second half of 1962. The order intake improved substantially over the year. Although APV's market share in heat exchangers was falling, sales of a number of new products recently introduced by the company were increasing rapidly.

This was particularly the case with in-place cleaning and automation. It was accordingly decided to take this out of Research and Development and establish a separate technical sales Automation Engineering Department (AED) under Harry Cooper, who had been in charge of the development in the Design Department.

For some time it had been apparent that APV's export business needed more expert handling than could be given by the one or two people in the Export Department working with the normal staffs in the home sales departments. At the end of 1962, the Board decided in principle to establish an autonomous Export Company as a subsidiary of the APV Company. Exports, after all, accounted for nearly half the output of the Crawley factory. Accordingly A.P.V. Exports Ltd[1] was set up in the middle of 1963 with Madron Seligman as Managing, and Bill Blois Johnson as Sales Director.

The improved market trend in early 1963 was reflected by APV-Paramount who were able to cease a four-day week and go on to full-time working, but orders were still low compared with the previous year until the newly licensed centrifugally-spun tube started to sell in the autumn. By then the foundry was selling more than twice as much outside the group as to the parent company whose needs it had been set up to supply.

The APV Company order intake for 1963 was a record at over £5 million so that, with work in progress reduced, the company could face the coming year with equanimity, but there was still concern about the fabrication shops. There the orders had continued low and, if this continued, then redundancies were in prospect. Such work as was obtained was against fierce competition and at very poor prices.

These conditions had affected Blackpool who depended on APV sales for much of its work, and a loss was made, half in the new

[1]Soon after changed to A.P.V. International Ltd.

190

Marton factory and half in the Cleveleys machine shop which had not been able to get going properly.

During 1963, Associated Industrial Consultants (AIC) were retained to investigate the problem of long deliveries. They suggested a reorganisation of the works into four separate sections corresponding to the main categories of manufacture, each to be run as a separate, autonomous product group. Some extension of production space would be required as well as a good deal of re-siting of machines.

It was decided to accept the recommendations of AIC's report. It did not produce any striking change in delivery times. But it prepared the way for the use of a computer in stock control and it streamlined the channels of production. As usual with such reports, it served to force people to make up their minds between alternative courses of action. As such it performed a useful function.

As a result of the AIC consultant's report, more space was required in the factory. It was obtained by erecting a new extension building behind the engineering shops bringing the total up to 400,000 square feet. It was ready in mid-1965 and the rearrangement of the shops could take place. At that time the rest of the land was rented so that APV now controlled the whole Crawley site.

Towards the end of 1963, APV was approached by W. J. Harwood, owner, with his family and associates, and Managing Director of Spiro-Gills Ltd, to buy his firm. It manufactured under licence air-cooled heat exchangers, mainly for the oil and chemical industries, at Pulborough and in a jointly owned plant at Blanc Miseron in France. The industrial logic of the take-over was clear, the financial status and results satisfactory and its prospects good. In spite of some undesirable features of the American licence it was agreed to acquire Spiro-Gills for £660,000 paid by the issue of 300,000 new APV ordinary shares, thus bringing the issued capital up to £2,850,000, the remainder being paid in cash from reserves. The deal was completed on 30 April and Spiro-Gills contributed over £50,000 to the group profits in 1964.

Harwood stayed on as Managing Director, but almost immediately fell ill and died in February 1965. After some interim appointments, his place was taken by Alister Menzies, who had joined the Spiro-Gills Board in November 1964 on his return from the United States.

For the rest of the group, and particularly for the Crawley companies, 1964 was a very good year. Sales were up by 25% over the previous year and profit exceeded the million mark for the first time. It had thus increased five-fold since 1957. More significantly profit on sales had increased to 11.4% from 6.1% in 1958 and on capital employed to 16.8% from 7.0%. An increased dividend of 17½ % was paid on the ordinary shares. Export sales amounted to over half the APV Company's output; United States, Spain, Germany, Australia and Japan were the largest markets.

Not only was output at a record level; so were orders booked both by the APV Company and by APV-Paramount, while APV Exports' orders were up 30% on the previous year.

At the beginning of the year there was still concern about keeping the coppersmiths fully employed. However, these fears were allayed by several large fabrication orders and by the middle of the year a high level of activity existed throughout the factory. From then on all was relatively plain sailing. At the half year all the overseas subsidiaries were doing well with the exception of India, where APVEC had run into a recession in its first year as a public company. SSP was also showing relatively poor results. In spite of this and the necessity to reserve against possible losses on contracts, the flow of sales ensured that excellent results would be achieved.

The order intake for the year of over £6 million was a record for the company. Backed by this, 1965 started well, although there were the perennial difficulties of recruiting skilled craftsmen and qualified draughtsmen and the working hours had been reduced from forty-two to forty-one hours per week.

Nevertheless, the company was well on the way to another record year when Will Jenkins relinquished the chair at the Annual General Meeting in May 1965.

## Development

This was a time of generally successful development, much of it still of substantial commercial value after twenty years or so. The Research and Development Division entered the period severely cut down in numbers and with several unwanted and unprofitable projects around its neck. As a result of a deliberate policy to extend new product development, it ended the period substantially expanded, much more closely integrated into the organisation and with a number of increasingly successful products to its credit.

Early in 1961, it had become clear that Hugh Goodman would not be able to carry on for long because of ill health. He retired at the end of the year and, with him, the company lost its most imaginative designer still, as he had shown with the plate evaporator and the new ranges of heat exchangers, commanding his old flair to a remarkable degree. It was decided to replace him with a Chief Engineer who would take responsibility for engineering throughout the company and direct the Drawing Office. As such it was thought that he should be in the Production Division. In July 1961 M. J. ('Julian') Kemper was appointed.

By 1963, the service work on plate evaporators had become so heavy, both in advice to the sales departments and in trouble-shooting, that a special evaporator 'Commando' was established under Kemper to relieve the Design Department.

In the middle of that year, there was a succession of mechanical engineering failures of one kind and another. It was decided that the company needed strengthening on the design side and, to that end, Kemper and his staff were transferred from Production to R&D. The evaporator 'Commando' was expanded into a permanent Evaporator Section to co-ordinate all the engineering work on evaporators in the Sales and Production Departments with Development and to handle commissioning and field trials.

The Research and Development Division now consisted of a Process Engineering Department under David Shore, an Engineering Department under Julian Kemper with Usher's Design

193

Department responsible to him, and the Laboratories under Botham.

The most far-reaching development in plate heat exchangers at this time was not taken by APV at all, though it had far-reaching effects on the company's development policy. Ljungström, working with Curt Rosenblad, patented in 1953 a form of plate consisting of small troughs pressed in a chevron or diagonal pattern to form a criss-cross matrix. Provided such a plate was pressed with sufficient accuracy, it had support points wherever one trough crossed another and so could be made extremely strong, even in very thin materials. The machine came on the market in 1958 and, although not fully realised at the time, it revolutionised the design of plate heat exchangers, particularly for the chemical industry, for it allowed the demand for larger sizes and higher pressures to be met even in costly materials like titanium. When Alfa-Laval acquired Rosenblads Patenter AB in 1963, the competitive screw was really on.

Already at the end of 1958 Goodman had produced some general ideas on a new range of heat exchangers. Design was started and by mid-1960 preliminary tests on the plate form had been carried out. It was based on crimped, shallow, horizontal troughs with a large number of support points where one trough crossed another. The tightening load was thus taken on the plates, not the rubbers. This was the prototype of the R5 plate.

It was soon apparent that the progressive pressing of one trough after another, as used for the other APV plates, was not suitable. The company had no press large enough to press the plates in a single stroke, however.

At this point the whole development was in jeopardy but, in mid-1961, the decision was made to buy a second-hand 3,500 ton press from Woolwich Arsenal to press other plates in a single stroke. Eventually, the production engineering and metallurgical problems were overcome sufficiently for the R50 machine, with a stainless steel frame, to be put on the market at the end of 1962, though with some misgivings. Other types of frame followed immediately after. These were capable of withstanding 225 psi and so were suitable for high throughput beer pasteurisation and UHT heating, as well as a variety of general industrial duties.

After a slow start, the R5 proved to be a very successful machine, mainly in the food and beverage, and comparatively less in the heavy industrial and chemical, fields. The main reason for this was that the plates could not then be pressed in titanium or nickel alloys.

Just at this time a market survey of industrial uses for plate heat exchangers had been commissioned. It suggested that a suitable plate must be available in these materials with solvent-resistant gaskets, capable of handling larger flows with lower pressure drop. Development of such a machine started in mid-1965. A great deal of work had already been done by Botham on developing improved rubbers, both in form and in heat and solvent resistance, including asbestos-based gaskets for the HX and R5 plates.

In the USA a demand had arisen for plates with a mirror finish. This could not be obtained with normal scratch polished sheet but when, in 1958, smooth cold rolled sheet came on to the market it was possible to meet the demand, and the Paragon finish was put on sale at a premium. It was hard to find the necessary polishers so, in 1961, a huge automatic polishing line was installed. Only six years later this became redundant with the availability of bright annealed sheet but it had paid its way by then.

An interesting proposal at this time was one from the Government's Warren Spring Laboratory to put heat exchanger calculations on to a computer. They demonstrated its feasibility but it was not possible to go further until the company had a computer of its own and a specialist to work it.

The plate evaporator had now started to sell extremely well. This brought a lot of extra work for R&D in trouble-shooting, in redesign in the light of experience and in developing new applications. Much of this was due to the combination of lack of fundamental knowledge with pushing the plant up to and eventually beyond the limits of satisfactory operation. As a result there were cases of several plants at a time failing for the same reason because at the time of sale the limits had not been determined.

This was just one aspect of the effects of the rapid increase in size of units that was occurring at this time. Costs of tooling and production, engineering difficulties (production and chemical as well as mechanical), and the time and inflexibility of development, all increase much more than in direct proportion to size. This was only just beginning to be appreciated by the R&D staff, let alone by the sales people or management.

In addition, unexpected operating difficulties arose and had to be dealt with in situations impossible to rectify at that stage.

This costly empirical approach did, however, provide the information on which to base the design of larger and much more efficient plates and separators.

In spite of the troubles, the plate evaporator was being a great commercial success. Eleven were sold in 1958, twenty in 1959 and forty-five in 1960, of which nearly three-quarters went to twenty-three countries overseas. After Britain, the USA was the largest market. The hundredth machine was sold in mid-1961 and the two hundredth in mid-1963. They had been used for an enormous variety of duties but mostly in the food and biotechnological industries.

A great deal of effort was also expended on continuous brewing. Technically, the able team under David Shore achieved a great deal but the resultant plant and processes did not offer sufficiently great advantages for brewers to feel that they should take the risk of using different and unfamiliar methods on existing plants. That this was so, followed largely on British and, to a lesser extent, Continental brewers realising, as the Americans had realised long before, that they were not getting the best from their existing plant and that many of them could double the output of their existing brewhouses by simply doing twice as many brews a day, in which case the fermenting rooms and storage tankage would become the bottlenecks. Interest, therefore, tended to shift during this period to continuous fermentation. Continuous brewhouses were only likely to be attractive in new breweries.

The CWB process was the one link in the brewhouse chain that might have succeeded on its merits for the heat and hop savings could be large. Although it was tried out on a pilot scale in several breweries, it always ran into difficulties and so never achieved commercial success.

In 1959, a consortium had been formed with the Brewing Industry Research Foundation at Nutfield, Guinness and Courage & Barclay jointly to develop continuous mashing processes. In 1961 this was enlarged to include wort boiling and further investigations were undertaken. A certain amount of success was had with various boiling processes but not enough to improve on an automated batch process first developed by Guinness that became, *faute de mieux*, the accepted method.

Continuous mashing and wort filtration went much better for the problems were more mechanical than biochemical. The plant as finally evolved consisted of a tube masher linked to a rotary filter.

Several semi-commercial plants were installed, on one of which at Guinness (Park Royal), a test run was successfully conducted for six months on end. They all ran satisfactorily and produced various types of worts in excellent yield, substantially indistinguishable from those from the normal batch process.

Nevertheless, it was felt that the plant, particularly the mash filter, was unreasonably complex mechanically and, although in early 1963 there were a number of enquiries, no British brewers installed a plant.

Guinness in the meantime had developed their own drum masher and belt mash filter and in mid-1962 ordered APV to manufacture a packaged plant to handle three barrels per day of their stout, linked to automated batch boiling and continuous stirred tank fermentation, worth £100,000 in all. This was thought to be simpler mechanically than the APV process and the line ran well for an extended period at higher than nominal throughput but it was never repeated.

At the same time work had been proceeding on continuous fermentaion. As early as 1958 Eric Watson and T. F. S. ('Freddie') Cooper, then his assistant in the Brewery Engineering Department, had done some experiments on fermentation in a tube in Watson's bathroom. Gradually the idea evolved into that of a tower in which the yeast was suspended and in which a concentration gradient was maintained that corresponded to the change of concentation with time in a batch fermenting vessel. Thus it could be expected to give at least a very similar flavour. It could also be shown to give a substantially higher rate of fermentation per unit volume than the batch process. If a somewhat higher temperature could be used then the fermenting efficiency could be still further increased. It looked attractive economically.

The results of preliminary laboratory work were very promising and on this basis a small-scale tower was put to work at Oranjeboom Brewery in Rotterdam (now part of Allied Breweries). Again results were good and the Dutch tower was scaled up and ran successfully for three months. A number of other larger towers were installed in Britain and on the Continent. All operated well except that there began to be some doubts as to the flavour. Nevertheless, a standard commercial unit was designed and the first unit was put to work at Mitchells and Butler's in mid-1964 with one at Oranjeboom following shortly after.

At this point a Spanish brewery, La Cervecera del Norte, although there had been some flavour problems with the pilot tower, ordered a complete continuous brewery, the largest brewery order ever taken by the company, to go to work in 1966 near Valencia. All the efforts of the R&D team were dedicated to engineering this project.

One other brewery development foreshadowed important changes. The use of a plate evaporator for wort concentration was demonstrated in America and a large installation ordered, the first step in high gravity wort production.

The possibilities of automation were just starting to be realised but they developed fast.

In 1958 the first commercial in-place cleaning installations were just going to work. At an ice-cream factory not only were tanks and pipework cleaned in-place under automatic control but the control of mix ingredients, pasteurisation and handling of mix were all under the direction of a control panel. Standard fully automatic cleaning units were successfully developed and sold for the dairy industry.

Attention was also turned to breweries and fruit juice installations. As a result of pilot tests on soft drinks, a large order was laid for an installation with visual control panels and including 366 automatic control valves. This was by far the most ambitious scheme so far and, as APV's first modern automation scheme, pointed the way for the future. Then in 1962, the first of several large automation orders, involving 440 automatic valves, came from Morinaga Milk Industries of Tokyo who already had a number of APV installations.

After a lot of work, the cold cleaning of brewery vessels was successfully carried out and the way was clear for the automation schemes in breweries that have formed such an important part of APV business since then. Automation, too, was being applied in the UHT Ultramatic plants.

It was now clear that this was going to be a major area of expansion for the company but, for the time being, it was a period of new applications of existing knowledge and not of the development of new products.

Automation required automatic on/off valves. Harry Cooper, who was in charge of cock and valve design, realised that rotary cocks were altogether too unreliable and set to work to design a linear moving, air-operated, automatic valve. The Zephyr valve was on the market in 1960 and the success of APV automation dates from then. The original design proved unsatisfactory in some applications, particularly at Morinaga, however. A redesign was started in 1964, and further modifications were intoduced as a result of Morinaga's criticisms but the new and much improved valve was not on the market until 1966.

Cocks, valves and fittings business had blossomed and, by the end of 1961, was running at £850,000 a year, about a sixth of Crawley's output. The troubles with the SP fittings had been overcome but it never quite swept the market as it was hoped it would do.

An International Dairy Federation Committee had been considering a European standard for fittings and in 1960 fixed on the company's SP fitting somewhat modified. This was hailed as a great opportunity for the company but, in fact, proved rather a mixed blessing. The modifications involved much bigger changes in design and manufacture than had been expected, so much so that a far-reaching programme of investigation of the properties of expanded fittings was undertaken. It led to important changes in design and expanding techniques and provided a joint with a strength virtually equivalent to welding, so eliminating welded bends and tees. These new 'ISS' fittings were on the market in mid-1963.

Although a number of plants replacing normal pasteurisation units had been supplied to Japan, fifty of them to Morinaga, the UHT process had had only limited application until 1964 when Tetra-Pak of Lund in Sweden put on the market their method of sterile filling into tetrahedral cartons, a brilliant development that, with the subsequent Tetra-Brik, still dominates the field.

At once, the possible market for long-life UHT milk was transformed and further development was undertaken, in the first place to provide a plant with fully automatic control of sterilisation, start-up, operation and shut-down including the links to the Tetra-Pak filler. For the first time a biological process had to be regulated absolutely by the accuracy of time and temperature control for, with the degree of 'sterility' required – less than one organism per 1000 containers – ordinary methods of bacteriological control were totally unacceptable.

The indirect-heated Ultramatic was developed and a first plant installed at the Express Dairy Company's Morden depot. After some modifications, it worked well and much was discovered about the factors affecting flavour.

Even before that, questions had been raised about the effect of heating time on the taste of the product. In particular, it was claimed that direct steam injection, as used in the Uperiser developed by Alpura in Switzerland and the first to operate with Tetra-Pak, gave a much improved taste although this was never substantiated. There was, however, some evidence of longer runs.

A weak point of the original APV Ultramatic was the complexity and consequent unreliability of the automation. Another prototype unit, installed in Hamburg, ran into continuous trouble and eventually was replaced by a modified unit designed by Holstein und Kappert. Certainly the difficulties of automating this type of plant had been badly underestimated and it was some time before they were overcome.

Using high-pressure models of the HX, HMB and R5 heat exchangers, beer pasteurisers were selling well but sterile filling was still a problem if large and costly tunnel pasteurisers were to be superseded.

No satisfactory method of sterile bottle filling existed. A far better bet was sterile keg filling. The market for keg beer was now developing fast. APV installed a number of units and an automatic plant was designed. Several were installed but insufficient development effort was put into it and it lost out to Burnett and Rolfe, a company that had been founded at the end of the war by two disgruntled APV employees and became a strong competitor especially in the fabrication of brewery vessels.

A new series of hygienic pumps, the PUMA range, was introduced. The basic design of pump was unaltered but it was so fitted as to permit greater flexibility in motor, seals and pump size together with a reduction in price.

The new range was on the market in 1959. It was an unspectacular, but highly successful, development. The range and uses of the

201

pump were steadily extended and, simple as it is, it has proved a best-seller for APV.

From the end of 1963, a good deal of effort was expended over several years in trying to develop a French process for the continuous production of cheese curd. It involved plate heat exchangers and evaporators, was claimed to give a better yield and, linked to machines under development in Australia for other steps in the process, gave promise of completely automated continuous lines for the production of cheddar cheese.

A special curd-producing machine, the Paracurd, was developed, manufactured and put to work, but the promised advantages were never realised and the investigation had to be dropped.

Business in soft-drinks manufacture was growing and a packaged pre-mix plant including de-aeration and carbonation was called for.

In 1961, Holstein und Kappert developed such a unit using HX plates with modified gaskets in which both de-aeration and carbonation took place in the plate pack without cooling. Several of these Carbomix units were installed in Germany operating with H u K's own high pressure fillers.

Later it was found that, with low-pressure fillers, the carbonation section had to be cooled. This removed the major advantage that the Carbomix process had over its competitors and gradually it was dropped.

While this was going on, work on the parameters governing carbonation directly in heat exchanger plates revealed that this could be done more simply and cheaply than in the Carbomix plant without restriction to high pressure fillers. This became the standard method for APV.

On a visit to America in 1960, Dummett had obtained basic information on methods of recovering the volatile flavouring essences that are otherwise lost in the evaporation of fruit juices (other than citrus for which no viable process then existed). Based on this, designs for units suitable for various fruits were worked out.

In 1962 a first plant went to work on Concord grape juice in the USA. Plants for other juices, including apple, were installed, all in conjunction with plate evaporators. Flavour recovery was now a standard APV product.

There was another rather unexpectedly successful fruit juice evaporator development. It proved possible to concentrate fruit pulps, free of pips and with added sugar, to jam. In practice most of these pulps are preserved with sulphur dioxide and a desulphiting unit had to be developed to avoid possible corrosion. This was achieved successfully in a modified de-aerator and the company now had a continuous jam plant. In 1964 it went on the market successfully.

The frantic search for products to license was modified and, indeed, both the Cooper valve and Rosenblad heat exchanger were relinquished following the take-over of the principals.

The search for a spray dryer continued, however. Anhydro of Copenhagen and another firm both approached APV in 1958 and a number of installations were examined critically. The choice was clearly in favour of Anhydro and an agreement for APV to manufacture and sell in Britain and certain other countries was signed in 1960. Thus started an association that was finally consummated when Anhydro joined the APV group in 1972.

APV-Paramount made several licence agreements of which by far the most important was that made at the end of 1962 with the ESCO Corporation of Portland, Oregon, for exclusive rights to their process for producing a thick-walled, seamless, centrifugally cast tube.

At this time the gas industry was starting to switch from coal carbonisation to the thermal cracking of petroleum naphtha and the demand for suitable tube for the cracking furnaces was growing rapidly, as it was also for furnaces in petrochemical plants.

A special department was set up to handle the business and the first order was taken in the autumn of 1963. In the foundry special revolving cylindrical steel moulds had to be laid down and set to work. In the APV Company methods were developed to weld sections together automatically and to machine them internally to give absolutely smooth, straight-bored tube assemblies.

This joint effort resulted in a product markedly better than its competitors and orders came in such volume as to transform Paramount's business.

### Sales and Marketing

Dairy plant continued to dominate the company's business, especially abroad. At home, there was a general overall increase though there were fears that rationalisation of the industry and reduction in milk production in 1964 would affect sales adversely – not apparently realised as far as APV was concerned. A more serious threat was acute price competition from Alfa-Laval, anxious to increase their share of the British market now that APV had lost the hold on the Swedish one that they had had before the war.

A number of important installations were made besides the usual complete towns' dairies at home and overseas. These were largely for milk products, ice-cream, UHT milk and automated process and cleaning control.

Apart from continuous brewing, other brewery business expanded, partly as a result of increasing rationalising of the industry – there were 440 UK brewery companies in 1950 and only 295 ten years later – but partly, no doubt, also to the good personal relationships between the brewery and APV management and staffs that had been developed.

As a result, the brewery sales were continually expanding and on two occasions large orders saved the company from a serious position. In April 1962, when overall sales had fallen badly, the £100,000 Guinness continuous brewing line did much to stabilise the position and, two years later, a very large order for brewery vessels from Bass, worth £123,000, saved the fabrication shop from redundancies.

The externally cooled fermenting vessels were a huge success. In two and a half years to the end of 1961, 260 vessels with a total capacity of 55,000 barrels were supplied to twenty-six brewery firms. Among a series of large orders, the most remarkable was an enormous uncooled fermenter of 8,016-barrel capacity (over 285,000 gallons or 4,600,000 bottles), welded on site at Guinness in Dublin in 1959. This was then, and still is, the largest beer fermenter in the world (Illustration 22).

The period was a traumatic one for the Chemical Engineering Division, including as it did a record year for orders and its final winding up as a contracting organisation.

It started well by the division turning a loss in 1957 into a profit for 1958, its first year in Crawley. In this year it took a large order for a new continuous benzole plant for Appleby-Frodingham at Scunthorpe, the site of the first such plant installed in 1940. In mid-1959 Webb resigned and was replaced by J. L. ('John') Sweeten, a chemical engineer of wide experience.

A few months before, the big Laporte peroxide plant, with its huge aluminium columns and vessels and CED-designed distillation plates, had successfully gone to work. As a result of these and other substantial orders, the invoiced sales and profit for 1959 were both up.

With the change in management and time spent on start-ups, however, the order intake for 1959 was very poor; there was no one to do any selling. As a result, in spite of the commissioning of two continuous benzole plants at Scunthorpe and an alcohol distillery in Ghana, the turnover for 1960 was less than half that for the previous year and the division only just about broke even.

Sweeten, therefore, went out for all the orders he could get. As a result, the order intake for 1960 topped £1 million, a record. First, there was a big contract for British Celanese, now merged with Courtaulds, at Spondon to recover pure aromatics by the pseudo-azeotropic process, used at Glasgow for toluene during the war, from highly contaminated condensates from their naphtha-cracking plant, part of the first petrochemical plant ever installed in Britain (in 1942). Other large orders followed including yet another continuous benzole refinery to handle the output from the great new steelworks at Llanwern (Illustration 23). It was the last order for such a plant APV was to take.

In April 1962, however, Peter Seligman was reporting that no orders had been received for several months and the division's future was causing concern.

By now it was clear that the Spondon plant now being commissioned was in real trouble. In the initial negotiations Sweeten had been pressed to knock £50,000 off his quotation and had skinned the specification to the bone. All this was unnecessary. He would have got the order in any case if he had stuck to his guns. As a result, although the process and main items of plant were working well, there was no chance as it stood of the guarantees being met in full.

Courtaulds presented a required list of plant alterations. It was quite reasonable. There was no alternative but to agree to carry it out. In return, Courtaulds waived the original guarantees provided the plant worked to their satisfaction. Great efforts were expended and by October the plant was operating profitably and an agreement had been reached with Courtaulds to settle their account. This was a satisfactory outcome, but the total cost to the company had been about £70,000.

In the meantime, several other plants, including Llanwern, had been successfully started up without serious trouble. Nevertheless, the division was going to show a small loss in 1962 and, owing to the total lack of orders, a much more substantial one in 1963. It was therefore decided in November to amalgamate CED with the Industrial Engineering Department (IED) under Bill Jones as Manager. It was not to handle further large contracting jobs other than those involving a reasonable proportion of APV equipment.

The joint department started by suffering a small loss. It was saved by a strange circumstance. In September 1963 there was a serious explosion and fire at the Spondon plant, and APV had to repair and rebuild it. It was on stream again in seven weeks. The profit from this remarkable operation set the department on its feet.

Thus CED came to an end. It had always been something of a misfit in the APV organisation, in spite of its notable achievements, and it had never really been able to compete with the large contracting organisations.

A number of important industrial fabrication jobs were carried out by IED, some in aluminium. The big methane tank at Canvey and its associated pipework went to work in early 1959. In 1962, another tank of twice the diameter, nearly 100 feet, was ordered. This contract, worth £360,000 in all, came at a most opportune time when orders were getting very short. It was by far the largest container ever built by APV.

Manufacture went well but when it came to be tested in 1964 there was a failure of some plastic components anchoring the tank inside the lagging and outer steel shell. Remarkably there was no fracture or explosion and no one was hurt, but there was a heavy bill for repairs. Since then, methane has come from the North Sea and there has been no more LNG work for APV.

A number of research atomic reactors were made. These demanded very high standards of fabrication and welding and were often enormously (and unnecessarily) complex. Several of them were exported. This work was never adequately remunerative and did not, perhaps fortunately, get the company deeply involved in atomic energy.

As Crawley's export trade had grown to such a large volume, it was involving an appreciable proportion of the efforts of members of the Board. Matthews and Peter Seligman travelled far and often on sales promotion in every part of the globe and Benson spent much of his time looking after the overseas subsidiaries.

The formation of A.P.V. Exports Limited as a fully-owned subsidiary of the APV Company in 1963 did much to relieve the pressure. As an autonomous, self-contained unit, it was able to deal more effectively with export problems and to give quicker and better service to overseas agents.

Among the overseas subsidiaries, Société APV in Paris did well. Its profit doubled from 1957 to 1962. Although profits fell somewhat in 1964, the take-off from Crawley increased and so did the total turnover.

Henry Lawless retired as Managing Director of Société APV due to ill health at the end of 1960, after a distinguished career. He was succeeded by W. ('Bill') de Ruyter, a brilliant young engineer who had joined the company in 1952. In 1963, it was decided to relinquish the offices in Paris and move to a totally new site. Bill de Ruyter started a search, but it was some years before the final move was made to Évreux in Normandy.

It was decided to set up a selling company for Benelux to supervise the operations of agents in those countries and to promote the sales of equipment to be manufactured in Belgium as well as that drawn from Crawley. It was thought that this could best be achieved by acquiring Luksano S.A., the company's agents in Brussels and setting up a new subsidiary company there.

However, it was soon apparent that the antagonism between the Dutch and French-speaking countries had been much underestimated. A Brussels-controlled company was just not acceptable to Dutch customers. It was therefore decided to set up a new subsidiary in Holland, and in 1965 APV Nederland started operation in Aalsmeer. A year or two later it was merged with the Merkens interests and Wim Merkens, 'old' Merkens' son, took over the general management.

Spain's industry was starting to boom and it was clear that APV was not getting its proper share of the business because of the need for local manufacture. Early in 1963 it was decided to set up a new associated company, APV Iberica, in Madrid in conjunction with Alto Vacio, a firm manufacturing high vacuum equipment, and ACOEX, the company's existing agents, with Luis Miranda as its volatile and able Managing Director. At this stage the company held 50% of the equity though this was increased to 51% three years later. A substantial increase of Spanish business resulted almost immediately.

APV-Italia's premises had become too cramped. A new office and shop were opened at the end of 1964 and Giovanni Marenghi took over as Managing Director, a position he has held ever since.

A.P.V. Company Incorporated did steadily increasing business with rising profits up to 1962. As almost all their turnover came from Crawley plant this was doubly profitable. They did especially well with plate evaporators under their Chief Engineer, Derek Dinnage. He was to prove a tower of strength to the growing subsidiary.

There were good sales of Paraflows to the USA breweries. In fact the R50 was given its first public showing at the International Brewing Exposition in Chicago.

In spite of its overall success, A.P.V. Company Inc. had to sell dairy equipment through 'jobbers' (internal agents) in order to cover the vast areas involved and consequently found it difficult to compete with larger firms like Alfa-Laval or Cherry Burell, who were able to sell direct. Following a proposal of D. G. ('Don') Colony, President of the Gaulin Corporation, it was agreed to set up a joint selling company, Associated Dairy Equipment Manufacturers (ADEM) to market the Manton-Gaulin homogeniser, APV heat exchangers and complementary equipment in the USA.

As a result APV in Buffalo lost its dairy business at a stroke and had to concentrate on the brewery and industrial markets. Not surprisingly, the sales and profit for 1963 were down, especially as there was little activity in plate evaporators, but from then on the company did remarkably well making a record profit with greatly increased turnover in the following year.

At the beginning of 1964, Alister Menzies resigned and J. B. ('Jim') Shanahan, an American Irishman whose good humour was combined with first-class business ability, succeeded him.

In Canada a new sales office and warehouse had been opened in Rexdale, a suburb of Toronto, in 1959 and Alister Menzies took over the presidency and directed the company from Buffalo.

The Canadian operation had now turned the corner, so much so that, by the beginning of 1964, it had to move into new premises in Weston, near Toronto. The change in fortunes occasioned by giving up manufacture had been remarkable; the net worth of APV's holding had increased sevenfold and prospects for the future were good.

The Brazilian company made a satisfactory profit in 1958 and the APV loan was liquidated by the issue of shares. Early in 1959 Robinson, now Managing Director, proposed putting up a new and larger factory. It was likely to prove a good investment because, owing to devaluation and taxation difficulties, it had become improvident to pay dividends to the parent company. By 1961 it was in operation.

All this time, good profits were being made although, owing to the devaluation of the cruzeiro, it was thought prudent not to consolidate the results. As a result of the new factory profit doubled from 1961 to 1962 in pounds in spite of devaluation, and so it continued. The factory was proving a good investment indeed. The internal inflation was becoming enormous, however, and in early 1964 the consequent devaluation was such that although the profit for that year in cruzeiros was much increased, yet it had decreased in sterling.

During this period a large number of installations were made that put APV do Brasil in a dominant position in the dairy and brewery industries there.

APVEC continued to operate well in India in spite of various financial and political difficulties so that its production, and with it its profits, steadily increased from 1958 to 1961.

The increase in output was overloading the factory and a 50% increase in space was undertaken in 1961, together with new equipment. Dum-Dum was now the leading shop of its kind in the country.

The expansion of business demanded further capital. APV was loath to increase its financial commitment in India but it proved impossible to find suitable Indian participants. It was therefore decided, in October 1962, to bring in local capital by a public issue which would leave APV holding some 55% of the equity. After several delays the issue was finally made in January 1964 and was twice subscribed.

In that year demand fell, and with it production and profit, but it was possible to pay a satisfactory dividend. Business improved in 1965 and APVEC was back on course.

In 1959, the World Dairy Congress was held in London. One of the many visitors to Crawley was Dr Kai Okada of Morinaga, an engineer of remarkable vision and ruthless determination to secure the highest standards. His ideas and the relationship between Okada and the Crawley staff personally were to have a considerable influence on dairy development at APV over the next decade or so.

Trade with Japan, especially with Morinaga for UHT plants, plate evaporators and then automation schemes, grew fast. In 1963 a new associated company, APV Kabushiki Kaisha, was established in Tokyo as a 50-50 joint venture with APV's agents there, the American Trading Company. The new company had an excellent start and returned good results in its first two years of operation.

In 1967, the Managing Director returned to Crawley and was replaced by Harry Cooper who had established very close relations with Morinaga over the big automation contracts and developments. At about the same time American Trading sold their shareholding to APV Holdings.

As Australia was an important market for Crawley products, the Board in 1959 started considering how best to invest further there. They favoured a merger between APV (Australia)-Bryant Proprietary Ltd and James Bell of Melbourne, a major, but largely complementary, competitor to the Bryants. Negotiations started, but fell through, so a public flotation was decided on and, in 1961, APV (Australia)-Bryant Pty Ltd was converted into a public company, Bryant Brother (Holdings) Limited.

211

Within six months of the flotation, Bell's raised the matter of a merger once again. There followed a remarkable series of negotiations that lasted a good three years but finally, early in 1965, the merger to form Bell-Bryant Limited took place. The APV holding was now reduced to 19%. It was to be more than ten years before APV recovered a majority shareholding.

At the Annual General Meeting on 20 May 1965, Will Jenkins resigned as Chairman but remained a member of the Board. Peter Seligman was elected to take his place, and Peter Benson became Deputy Chairman. There were other changes in the APV Company management at the same time. Henry Pickard retired and was replaced by Eddie Cash as Works Director. At the same time, Jack Matthews, who had been awarded the OBE for services to export in 1962, announced his intention to give up his post as Sales Director in October 1965. He was not replaced directly; Tony Dummett became Deputy Managing Director with responsibility for the Sales and Marketing Divisions as well as the R&D and engineering activities.

So a Seligman returned to the chair of the APV Company to see it through the last phase of this history. It was now no more than the largest subsidiary of a prosperous international group and its relative importance in it was to decrease as the group grew steadily in the future. But it was still at the seat of central authority, responsible for major technical development and supplying a reserve of marketing and management expertise. As such it continued to exert a pre-eminent influence on the group.

That the company had reached this position was largely the result of Will Jenkins' wise and far-sighted guidance. His influence was unobtrusive but none the less decisive.

## Chapter 11
# Peter Seligman's Chairmanship 1965–1977

In this last period events have moved from an area that can justifiably be regarded with the cold glance of history to one of contemporary comment. It must be treated rather differently for several reasons.

In the first place, new and important external trends were taking place – much increased inflation, fluctuations in the value of the pound, the discovery and exploitation of North Sea gas and oil and the increase in power of the trades unions, among them. Their ultimate effect is unpredictable.

Internally, too, the changes were great. The acquisition of a number of major undertakings in quick succession affected, as it was bound to do, not only the status of the APV Company within the group but the pattern of its business. The Kestner Evaporation and Engineering Company of Greenhithe in 1966 provided plastics fabrication and know-how on tubular evaporators that had to be integrated with the company's expertise on plate machines. After Clarke-Built was acquired, the manufacture of their ice-cream freezers and swept surface heat exchangers was incorporated in the Crawley operation only to be eliminated when Crepaco joined the Group six years later in 1973, bringing with them their much more sophisticated machines. The L. A. Mitchell Group in 1969 transformed the APV distillation business by bringing in the licence for the Glitsch tray that had been a serious competitor of West and by providing a replacement for CED in their Process Contracting Division so that distillation work, as such, practically disappeared from the Crawley shops. Burnett and Rolfe in 1973 brought in excellent brewery keg sterile filling equipment as well as extending the group's fabrication capacity for large vessels.

All these acquisitions changed the operations of the APV Company. Others reinforced them, like the Gaulin Corporation and Anhydro, both in 1972. There were others, too, that had little direct effect on the APV Company's affairs, however important they might be in the group, like D. J. Osborne or Pratchitt Brothers, now APV-Mitchell Dryers.

The overseas subsidiaries and associated companies, particularly those in Australia, France, Japan and the United States, began to engineer large and complex contracts themselves and required less and less help from Crawley. Indeed, even in new products and in research and development, a reverse flow of ideas began to take place. More and more the tendency grew to establish particular companies as centres of excellence for certain technologies in the group; Crawley's particular spheres included heat exchange, evaporation, automation, sterile processing and large scale fabrication, though in none of these was their position an exclusive one.

An increasing proportion of the business, abroad as well as in Britain, was in the form of large overall contracts that, while they would be credited as a whole to one company in the group, would often incorporate plant items from others.

The Toni dairy in Zürich, commissioned in 1976, for example, contained automation and process plant from the APV Company but also three Anhydro spray dryers, five Crepaco ice-cream freezers, homogenisers from the Gaulin Corporation, an automatic plate ice-cream hardener from APV-Parafreeze (once Clarke-Built Williams) together with tanks and pipework provided by the company's agent in Switzerland, Gebrüder Ott. It could not have been engineered other than as a group effort (Illustrations 28 and 29).

Moreover, as the subsidiary companies undertook more and more of their own engineering, so they ordered more material from Crawley for stock and less specially designed for a specific duty. By

24. Peter Seligman and the Duke of Norfolk chatting to an apprentice on the occasion of the presentation of the Queen's Award to Industry for Export Achievement (1966).

25. Tony Dummett and David Shore taking delivery of APV's first scientific computer (1966). It was the first IBM 1130 produced in Britain.

26. (Above) A large multi-ef
plate evaporator installation at
Mersch in Luxembourg (1969).
is for the evaporation of butter
milk and skim milk.

27. (Left) Richard Seligman wi
first plate heat exchanger prio
its installation in the Science
Museum (1972).

*Facing page:*
28. (Above) Control room of t
fully-automated Toni dairy, Zü
(1977).

29. (Below) Pasteurisation area
the Toni dairy, Zürich (1977).
plate heat exchangers and Ga
homogenisers are prominent.

30. An R235 plate heat exchanger (1976). Inset: R235 plate showing chevron trough pattern used in the latest generation of heat exchangers.

31. Aerial view of the APV Crawley plant and offices (1977).

1975 the ultimate use of some 60% of the total export material from Crawley was not known when it was despatched.

Detailed figures of turnover, therefore, let alone of profit, would have little meaning in any case and even less when distorted by inflation. It will suffice to say that the group expanded nearly sevenfold in real terms over the period without diluting its return on capital which actually increased from 19% to 23%. The APV Company itself increased its turnover by about 70% in real terms while maintaining its profitability, though not without some fluctuations.

The pattern of the company's trade changed somewhat. Up to this time, the dairy business had been dominant with the brewery and industrial dividing the rest. At a group conference, including the chief executives from all the subsidiary companies, held in the summer of 1966, it was agreed that the chemical industry offered the widest scope for expansion and that policy should be directed to that end.

As far as acquisitions went this was achieved, for most of the companies incorporated in the group up to about 1970 had major interests in the chemical industry. For the APV Company it was not so easy. With the loss of the distillation and similar activities, most of the company's products were better suited to the food industries – with one exception, the plate heat exchanger. With the advent of the inclined trough plates and the ability to provide them in inherently expensive corrosion-resistant materials, such as titanium, at relatively low cost, plate machines began to be generally accepted in the chemical industry. So much so that by the 1970s the value of all machines sold world-wide for heavy industrial duties and to the chemical industry outweighed several fold that of all machines for the food and beverage industries. APV was running the risk of losing out in this growing market. Development was, therefore, directed to producing a range of models specifically designed for it.

Apart from plate machines, however, the APV Company itself did not benefit greatly from the change in policy. Then in the early

1970s came the oil crisis and a heavy cut-back in capital spending in the chemical industry so that more attention reverted to the food and beverage industries.

Abroad, the dairy industries in one form or another had remained the major interest, reinforced by the acquisition of Gaulin, Anhydro and, especially, Crepaco. At home, however, dairy business was relatively stagnant and it was the breweries that offered the greatest scope.

Concentration into large central units, the rapid increase in the lager beer trade and the need to economise in labour all demanded capital expenditure, particularly in automated equipment. In the early part of the period, brewery work accounted for only about a quarter of the home orders; by the end the proportion was over a half.

Another major change was technical. This was the era of automation and the computer for APV. The use of automatic control, first envisaged by Reg Cuttell and Harry Cooper, had grown rapidly and decisively. Instead of an occasional adjunct, it became first an essential feature and then the basis of design of any large new dairy, brewery or food plant. The elimination of processing error, the assurance of proper hygiene and the elimination of often unreliable labour made it a *sine qua non*.

For the company, this meant a major effort in seeing that a basic appreciation of automation techniques was absorbed by the sales force and that sufficient engineering, research and development was provided.

Mini computers found an essential place in automation schemes but, important as they were, their influence was as nothing compared with that of the scientific computer installed in the R&D Division in 1966 and the large commercial computer set to work two or three years later. It was perhaps less the speed and accuracy of computation that caused changes of outlook than the imposition of systems of rigid logic in, for instance, plate heat exchanger calculations or stock control and the consequent necessity to follow them through to their ultimate conclusions.

In the works, too, automation was increasing. Over the previous few years the introduction of a wide range of semi-automatic tools had revolutionised the company's machine shop operations. By 1966, Cash was advocating the use of fully automatic numerically controlled machines and a number were installed with considerable effect not only on productivity but on the organisation of short batch production.

To get the best from the new machinery it was necessary to agree with the workforce to permit semi-skilled labour to operate certain machines doing types of work previously reserved for skilled men on non-automatic machines, in return for some form of productivity agreement. Discussions started in 1965 and were enormously protracted. It was not until three years later that agreement was reached.

It was as well that reason prevailed for, over practically the whole of these years, the company continued to suffer from a shortage of skilled labour, both craft and qualified engineers, and needed to use as many less-skilled men as possible.

With such radical changes in the company's business, it was natural that the allocation of research and development resources should alter. Plate heat exchangers continued to demand the lion's share as the new range of industrial machines was evolved. Evaporators, too received a good deal of attention – falling film types, particularly.

In other areas the changes were marked. When Harry Cooper was transferred to head the Automation Engineering Department (AED) he took all the development work with him. A few years later, it became clear that it was not proving effective to combine sales support and automation design with development in the same department. When Cooper left for Japan, therefore, two men were transferred from AED to the Laboratory where excellent work was done.

In processs engineering, work on continuous cheese production, the continuous brewhouse and tower fermenters faded away as they failed to achieve substantial commercial acceptance. They were replaced by investigation of a range of ultra high temperature sterilisation processes and the auxiliaries to go with them.

At the same time, much of the purely engineering development, of valves and fittings for example, had been transferred from R&D to a new Engineering Division to leave the Design Department free to concentrate on new products.

This was part of a general reorganisation that took place when Peter Seligman took over the chairmanship from Will Jenkins and Jack Matthews retired as Sales Director. Both the Sales and the Research and Development Divisions were then each replaced by two new divisions.

The Sales Division was reconstituted as the Home Sales Division under Charles Brissenden and the Marketing Division with Bill Jones as Manager.

The Research and Development Division was under David Shore while a new Engineering Division was put under Julian Kemper as Chief Engineer.

Subsequently, the Engineering Division was hived off and incorporated with the main Drawing Office, Contracting Services and Proposals. This new autonomous Engineering Division, under Julian Kemper, who joined the APV Company Board, remained responsible to Dummett although eventually it was to find its way into the Production Division.

It was also decided to abandon the Executive, that for some ten years or so had controlled the day-to-day management of the APV Company, and to transfer its activities to the Board, strengthened by bringing Brissenden, Ted Clarke – now General Works Manager – Grover, Jones and Shore on to it. The management was now in a position to act more independently of the Holdings Board and from this point did so.

Abroad the company had a good year in 1965. France was the most important market, largely due to some major dairy contracts. The second largest market was Japan where Morinaga laid a contract for one of the largest automated complexes for the treatment of milk that had ever been installed anywhere. Other important markets were the USA, Australia, Eire and Germany. With the exception of Japan, where business fell off rapidly after 1972 when APV-KK and Morinaga parted company, this pattern of export business continued generally throughout the period.

Nevertheless, the year was one of some disappointment. A moderate increase in invoiced sales was barely enough to absorb additional costs.

Nor was 1966 any better. Turnover was virtually static in a year of very difficult trading conditions. Expenses increased and profit was down although for the group it was once more at a record figure as, indeed, it continued to be every year.

The continuous brewery at Del Norte, Valencia, was completed and commissioned, not without a good deal of difficulty. Eventually it was brought to the point of operating satisfactorily at its designed throughput but there remained some small differences in flavour of the beer as compared with the normal batch process that were never wholly resolved. After a year or two the company went into liquidation and the plant was closed down. Since then, it has been acquired by a company of greater technical sophistication and put to work again successfully until it became necessary to expand throughput, when it was switched to batch production.

This was the last continuous brewhouse installed by APV. Compared with a modern batch plant, fully automated and handling six or eight brews a day, its advantages in capital and operating costs were insufficient to outweigh its greater complexity and lack of flexibility. So ended what had looked like a world beater.

While the indirectly heated Ultramatic UHT plant gained increasing acceptance, the need had been felt for some time for a direct heated plant that was more acceptable to some overseas markets and offered the advantage of longer runs if at the expense of steam economy. The best known of such plants was the Uperiser, devised by Alpura and manufactured by Gebrüder Sulzer of Winterthur (Fig. 8). When, therefore, APV was approached by Alpura, agreement was soon reached with them and Sulzer to take over the world manufacturing and selling rights.

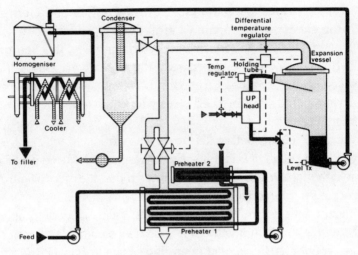

Fig. 8. Uperiser.

This immediately added substantially to the range of sterilising plant available to the company. It was a commercial success, but the amount of further development work needed was much under-estimated and the Uperiser and Ultramatic were to remain major R&D projects for years to come.

The most important development with plate heat exchangers was the installation of an IBM 1130 scientific computer (Illustration 25) and its application to their calculation.

The first commercial calculation had dramatic results. An order was being lost in Finland on price. The specification was fed to the computer which returned a number of plates one-third less than that reckoned by the human calculators. They confirmed the accuracy of the computation and the order was won. This experience demonstrated the unwitting conservatism built into trial-and-error hand calculations.

From then on, all possible calculations were done by computer and programs were soon worked out for more elaborate heat exchangers, evaporators, distillation columns, pressure vessels and a host of other computations.

At the Group Expansion Conference it had been decided to

expand the total research and development effort. In spite of various deflationary measures that were having to be adopted to correct falling profitability, the Board had the courage to go ahead with this policy.

More qualified staff were engaged and a new test house was erected on the northern perimeter of the Crawley site. It was occupied early in 1968 and provided about double the space so that it met at least most of the demands for testing new larger units. It was fully occupied almost immediately. By the autumn, David Shore and John Jackson were pressing for further building and at the end of October the Board authorised the construction of a new development shop next door. It was occupied at the end of the following year and group metallurgical facilities began to be set up in the old one. This was part of a move to provide group R&D facilities beyond the capacity of the smaller subsidiaries to maintain for themselves.

In 1966 the company became one of the first to receive the Queen's Award to Industry for Export Achievement (Illustration 24).

The following year, 1967, was not dissimilar, with the APV Company only barely doing better.

### Devaluation and its Effects

Towards the end of the year, the pound was devalued, something to which the British people were far from accustomed. It took the company initially by surprise but it was quickly realised that, though costs and therefore prices would have to increase, it would improve APV's competitiveness abroad and reduce that of its major European competitors at home. It certainly acted as a major factor in expanding sales in the following years.

An important licence was acquired, that for the Rosco evaporator, a falling film plate unit particularly suited for large industrial duties. It was invented by Curt Rosenblad and his son Axel in the United States, the last of a series of brilliant inventions by this remarkable entrepreneur. The Rosco has been at the core of a number of large APV installations both at home and abroad.

The first of the new range of industrial heat exchangers, the R6, was put on the market in 1967. This was a conventional medium-size machine capable of handling large flows, particularly aimed at the marine industry. It was followed by the R10, a larger version of the R6, which was immediately successful, especially as both of them could now be pressed in titanium.

In heat exchanger production attention was starting to fasten on pressing technique. The method of progressive troughing was wasteful of time and plant utilisation. R&D in their studies of a range of plates able to compete directly with the Rosenblad range, were also coming to the conclusion that only 'one-hit' pressing would be acceptable. For the larger plates under consideration, the pressing loads were likely to be quite beyond the range of the old 3,500-ton press. Moreover, this had broken down towards the end of 1965, causing much dislocation of production and deliveries and giving warning that its useful life was limited.

It was beginning to look as though a new, and possibly very expensive, press was going to be required. Then in September, 1968, the 3,500-ton press broke down again and simultaneously halted the production of R5 plates, now the best selling of the APV models, and all development pressings. It was repaired again without too long a delay but it settled the question of a new large press. A 20,000-ton machine was ordered in December.

Automation was by now the very backbone of the company's large contract business. The huge Tama dairy in Tokyo was a joint design effort of Harry Cooper with Okada. The automated tank room installed in Scottish & Newcastle Breweries' Holyrood, Edinburgh, plant was entirely the production of AED. These were typical of the large installations that were now to be undertaken.

In the new Automation Laboratory, W. H. Considine, working on an idea of Harry Cooper's, was starting the investigation that was to lead to the 'Highway' system of control wiring together with a mini computer, the heart of the complex automation contracts of the future, a brilliant piece of work in a field quite new to the company.

By 1968, trade was improving substantially. Invoiced sales were up 11%, profit even more and the new order intake exceeded all previous years by a large margin. While the dairy industry provided the main contribution to this improvement, business also expanded in other fields and several large orders were obtained (Illustration 26). Among these were a £1 million contract for a large highly automated plant to produce butter and skim milk powder at Alfreton in Derbyshire. This included a wide variety of group plant. There were also two large whisky effluent treatment plants.

A commercial computer was installed at the end of the year in the air-conditioned ground floor of a new office block built during the year.

The production space, too, was increased. At Crawley, a large tower building was erected behind the main shops for the vertical fabrication of silo tanks and large cylindrical fermenters. Production costs of what were becoming important lines were thereby notably reduced.

In October 1968, Peter Seligman ceased to be a Managing Director of the Holdings and APV companies leaving Peter Benson as sole Managing Director. Appropriately, 1969 opened with a further honour for him. He was awarded the CBE in the New Year's Honours List for 'services to export'.[1] It was an auspicious start to what was to prove a very successful year for both the group and the APV Company. Turnover and profit were both well up and that in spite of serious vicissitudes.

One of the most serious was a strike in the nickel industry in Canada which not only led to a large increase in the price of nickel but actually threatened supplies of nickel-bearing materials. The price of stainless steel advanced by more than 60% and material stocks had to be substantially increased.

Nevertheless, it proved possible to find the finance to acquire L. A. Mitchell (Holdings) Ltd, a group of companies supplying a range of plant and engineering services mainly to the chemical industries. The acquisition was to have a considerable effect on the APV Company, and indeed others in the group, mainly resulting from

[1] He was knighted at the beginning of 1978, just after he retired.

the serious difficulties experienced with the Croydon factory, once Metal Propellers.

As a result, there was a far-reaching reorganisation at the end of the year. Metal Propellers was amalgamated with the Contracts Division of APV-Kestner from Greenhithe. Ted Clarke was transferred from Crawley to become Works Director; while Bill Jones became Marketing Director.

Bill Jones thus left the sphere of the APV Company that he had served so faithfully in a number of mostly unrewarding jobs.

When Ted Clarke left for Croydon, Arthur Boyce was brought in as General Works Manager from Tube Investments.

The Clarke-Built operation at Chiswick was proving hardly viable on its own so, in October, it was transferred to Crawley. It proved a difficult transfer. The improvisatory fabricating and design methods of Clarke-Built did not fit readily into APV's more rigid organisation. Development was started and continued until the acquisition of Crepaco in 1973 made it superfluous.

There were also some exceptional problems mainly associated with commissioning the large evaporator contracts taken the year before. The two large whisky effluent treatment plants suffered a series of unexpected process difficulties. A lot of work led to plant modifications and much improved operation but this took several years to complete.

At Alfreton, a complex situation arose that nearly led to disaster. When the time came to start it up in the spring of 1969, it was found that for reasons outside APV's control it was not possible to handle the required input. The Milk Marketing Board, who owned the plant, threatened to have the plate evaporator removed. This was avoided but it was not until October 1971 that it was finally accepted.

With the failure of the French continuous curd process, the company lacked the entry to the cheese industry it had been seeking. Bell-Bryant, however, were developing large cheddar curd-handling machines. Only the curd production step was missing for the APV group to be able to engineer complete automated cheese factories.

The link was provided by N. V. Maschinefabriek Bijlenga-van der Ploeg who manufactured the 'Tebel' cheese vats at Leeuwarden in Holland. In mid-1969, a consortium was formed between the three companies, APV-Bell Bryant-Tebel, to secure contracts for complete cheese-making installations.

The commercial computer was now fully realising expectations. It was helping materially in stock and production control, and in handling cost and financial accounting. The engineers were already looking at computer-aided design. The predicted change in outlook was coming about.

The Junior heat exchanger, a small model intended for experimental work and very small throughputs was put on the market in 1969. It was remarkable as being the first APV plate with shallow chevron troughs (Illustration 30, inset). It was followed a few months later by the R405, a medium-sized machine and the first of APV's new generation of high-efficiency industrial heat exchangers.

In 1970 not only did trading conditions fluctuate disconcertingly both at home and abroad but the effect of a growing rate of inflation began to make itself felt in increased costs and reduced profit margins, especially with the long-term large contracts. So, although the APV Company's turnover went up, profit did not do so in proportion.

The first Rosco order was laid, an enormous multi-stage installation for grain whisky effluent at North British Distilleries worth £½ million with full mechanical vapour recompression. Much had to be learned about the new production methods devised for manufacturing the enormous dimpled plates, but the whole installation was a great success. A second installation was ordered a year or two later, so profitable had the first unit proved to be.

Early in 1971, after extended trials, the new 'Highway' system and mini computer was sold to Scottish & Newcastle for yet another in their series of automated brewing plants. It operated well and formed the basis of almost all the large automated plants that were to follow.

Continuous tower fermentation began to appear attractive commercially. There were several semi-commercial scale units at work but it had now become necessary to scale up still further if the process was to become fully competitive with large vertical cylindrical fermenting vessels and high gravity 'heavy' brewing. Two large batteries of tower fermenters were installed. While they operated quite successfully, they did not prove to have any major economic advantage so these were the last APV continuous fermentation plants.

During the year an extension filled in what remained of spare space on the Crawley site, to provide room for the new 20,000-ton press installed in the middle of 1971.

It proved even more of a giant than had been anticipated. It was erected and commissioned without incident and from then on fulfilled all expectations. The press not only permitted the production of much larger pressings than hitherto but allowed existing plates to be pressed much more efficiently and accurately, so improving the design and performance of plates and frames alike at a stroke.

As the company entered 1971, the outlook seemed promising except that it was almost impossible to assess the effect of inflation on industry; whether it would delay investment in capital equipment or cause APV prices to rise faster than foreign competitors were alike quite uncertain. Nevertheless, the APV Company and the International Company had a reasonable year with profits similar to the previous one's.

Sales of heat exchangers and plate evaporators abroad were specially good. By early in the year the total sales of plate evaporators since 1958 topped 700. About 44% had gone to the dairy industry and 24% to fruit juice processors. 80% were sold abroad in fifty-five countries with Germany the best market, followed by the USA, Japan and France.

In November, Eddie Cash retired from the APV Company Board after eighteen years in which he had been largely responsible for transforming the mechanical equipment of the works and the apprentice training scheme that was always very close to his heart. Arthur Boyce succeeded him on the APV Company Board, and as Works Director.

The company entered the following year, 1972, with some misgivings. Home business seemed to be stagnant. The brewery industry was not expanding its resources at the rate that it had done for the previous few years and the long-expected developments in the chemical industry still showed no signs of appearing. Had it not been for the buoyant export business, things would have looked black indeed; as it was, there was talk of short-time working and redundancies.

As it turned out, the markets for dairy, food, fruit juice and brewing equipment all picked up during the year. In the UK and Eire, as a result of their entry into the Common Market, there was substantial demand for milk process plant. Another important trend was a move in Europe towards ultra high temperature processing and aseptic packaging of various food products as well as milk.

But the year was dominated by a series of orders for large automated ice-cream plants, in Japan, Belgium, South Africa, the UK and Italy. The Motta plant near Naples was one of the largest orders ever taken by APV. It covered the computer-controlled preparation and processing of ice-cream mix to some 150 different recipes. It was APV's automation expertise that enabled it to break into this new market.

The Cheese Consortium was making large inroads into the market, mainly for Tebel vats and strainers, though it did install one complete plant that was remarkable for the degree of commercial collaboration involved.

It was for Donegal Milk Products at Letterkenny in Eire for the automated production of cheddar cheese, financed jointly by the Irish Milk Marketing Board and Mitsui in Japan who undertook to take half the output for several years. Okada acted as consultant and was largely responsible for the APV Group taking the main contract. It included equipment from APV, Tebel and Bell-Bryant.

APV-Mitchell's Process Contracting Division at Croydon took over as main contractor. In spite of so many organisations having a hand in it, the contract went surprisingly well. It was the most advanced small cheese plant in Europe.

So, after all, the APV Company and its international subsidiary had a good year with increased turnover and profits.

Dummett retired at the end of the year and Madron Seligman took his place as Deputy Managing and Marketing Director. Charles Brissenden succeeded him as Managing Director of APV International but remained Director in charge of home sales as well. Under him, Freddie Cooper became General Manager and Director of the export company while N. T. L. ('Norman') Garrett was made General UK Sales Manager of the APV Company.

On 20 September, Dr Richard Seligman died, appropriately enough quietly at his desk as he was getting ready to go home. Even at the age of ninety-four he travelled daily from London to Crawley and was a familiar figure as every day he walked around the works and laboratories that he had founded over sixty years before.

He was a much loved man and on 26 September, the workforce and staff at Crawley turned out to a man to salute his funeral cortège as, loaded with flowers, it drove him round the site for the last time.

It was only a month or two earlier that he had been at the Science Museum in South Kensington, not a stone's throw from the laboratories where he had first studied chemistry under Armstrong, to hand over his first plate heat exchanger for exhibition there (Illustration 27). It was a fitting resting place for his revolutionary brain-child.

## Group Expansion and its Effects

While his death marked the end of an epoch for APV, it also coincided with the beginning of a new one. During 1972 and the beginning of 1973, there were important changes in the composition of the APV Group. They marked the emergence of APV as a significant multi-national organisation. They also had important consequences for the APV Company itself.

In July, APV Holdings acquired the whole of the share capital of Anhydro and then, in October, of Burnett and Rolfe which had become the largest supplier of stainless steel tanks to the UK brewing industry as well as being a world leader in keg washing and racking equipment.

Then, negotiations that had been in train for some years to acquire the CP (Creamery Package) Division of the St Regis Paper Company were concluded in March 1973. Crepaco Inc., as it was now called, became a member of the APV Group and so redressed the balance of it towards the food industry with a much larger stake in North America.

This was the Golden Jubilee year of the invention of the APV plate heat exchanger. The company celebrated it by bringing out the R145, by far the largest yet manufactured by APV. It was ready just in time to be shown at the Achema in Frankfurt. Like the R4, the thin gauge plates were available in a range of highly corrosion resistant materials, for it was rightly believed that sales would largely be for high flow sea-water and effluent duties.

The year was one in which excellent results were achieved with heat exchangers as a whole. Indeed, it was a good year overall for Crawley. In spite of labour difficulties, turnover and profit were both up marginally.

This was a good performance in a year of political difficulties. A wage freeze caused serious dissatisfaction in both staff and workforce. The Israeli war in the autumn led to a catastrophic increase in oil prices by the OPEC countries and a consequent increase in inflation rate. Finally, general industrial unrest broke out associated with the miners' strike at the end of the year and the energy crisis that accompanied it.

The worst effects were not felt until early 1974 and in some ways they were even beneficial. The growing interest in energy saving and environmental control could only benefit the heat exchanger and evaporator business. Moreover, the direct effects were blanketed for the APV Company and some others in the group since they were licensed to work a five-day week because of the importance of their products to the food and energy industries.

The acquisition of Crepaco affected the APV Company's position within the group both directly and relatively. Crawley could no longer claim the same dominant position in the dairy and food industries, commercially or technically. The Crepaco ice-cream machinery immediately displaced the Clarke-Built. Crepaco at Lake Mills became the group centre for developing ice-cream and food processing equipment; leaving heat exchange, evaporation, automation and metallurgy to Crawley. Crawley, although possessing the largest and best equipped laboratories, no longer dominated the rest of the group, though the job of co-ordinating group R&D activities rested there.

Crepaco supplied other badly needed items like their positive pump, although some of their products, plate heat exchangers and homogenisers for example, were directly competitive with existing APV products. On the other hand, they afforded a new outlet for Crawley technology and products. They soon secured two significant dairy contracts based on APV automation.

While the relative importance of Crawley was diminished, this did not mean that its activities were to be reduced; they were to be concentrated on its strengths. Under a five-year plan, far from running down, the company was to be strengthened by new plant, methods and procedures.

The year was again a specially good one for the dairy industry, particularly overseas.

At home, the rush to install new cheese plant was fast running down as the profitability within the EEC became less attractive. A Bell-Siro continuous cheddaring plant was sold; otherwise there was little activity. In the United States, however, three continuous cheddar cheese lines were sold. The Consortium was now doing very well for Bell-Bryant but not particularly so for APV or Tebel who in any case were suffering from acute price competition.

Whey processing, on the other hand, had become of major

230

importance. A large evaporator and drying plant and two ion-exchange demineralisation plants were supplied.

Falling film tubular evaporators had long been the only serious competitors of the plate machines where short hold-up time was required. It was therefore timely that an APV falling film plate evaporator should now be launched. It had been two or three years in development and tests had confirmed that it gave higher capacity than the normal plate evaporator together with shorter holding time. It was particularly designed for highly heat sensitive products such as fruit juices and this is where it found its major application.

It was an important step forward when computer-aided design was introduced after several years' intensive development. It increased productivity at once, improved accuracy and eliminated much dull routine work.

By 1974 it had become clear that, with all the recent additions to the group, Peter Benson would be grossly overloaded if he were to remain Managing Director of the APV Company as well as of the group. At the beginning of June he relinquished his position to become Deputy Chairman. Dr K. A. G. ('Ken') Miller took his place as Managing Director with a seat on the Holdings Board. He had had a brilliant career as an engineer in ICI.

That year started dreadfully badly with production dislocated by the effects of industrial unrest and by shortages of labour and industrial supplies. Deliveries, always difficult in an organisation of APV's complexity, became very unreliable and staff morale, already badly affected by the wage freeze and general industrial uncertainty, fell. Costs were rising as a result of the energy crisis and overhead expenses had to be kept under strict control to avoid a critical cash flow situation.

Then came two elections and the uncertainty about Britain's continuing membership of the Common Market in face of the referendum that took place in the following year. The Board had no doubt of the way it ought to go.

Since Britain entered the Common Market, both orders and profit derived from the other eight members had advanced

231

significantly in real terms. In 1974, 38% of the large volume of export orders received by Crawley had emanated from the other EEC member countries. Jobs could be lost if exports to Europe fell as a result of leaving the Community.

Inflation, now rapidly accelerating, was having serious effects. By increasing direct and indirect costs, it made it more difficult to maintain the company's competitiveness overseas and it had created a business climate in the UK that notably failed to encourage capital investment as compared with other countries. This situation was reflected in Crawley's order book for the year in which over 60% came from overseas.

Nevertheless, the year was one in which demand exceeded supply with the production situation limiting the company's ability to translate a healthy order book into invoiced sales.

Under the circumstances, Crawley did extremely well to increase its output and its profitability substantially. The order book was more than sustained in real terms but for this APV had to thank the export company.

The plate heat exchanger business, in particular, jumped up, much of it due to the new big R145. Installations included a batch for cooling duties on a North Sea oil rig and large orders from the USA and Germany. These big machines with titanium plates brought in big money. They needed to do so, for development was long and costly, and the tooling very expensive.

Important dairy orders included that for the automation of the new Toni Zürich dairy, for which negotiations had been proceeding for four years; and for a computer-controlled ice-cream plant for Unilever's Italian subsidiary.

In the home market, however, the dairy business was falling away from the high level of the two previous years. Farmers were reluctant to produce milk at the ruling price when faced with the enormously increased costs of feeding stuffs so that numbers of livestock were reduced. The consequent underproduction was compounded by a consumer subsidy that resulted in increased sales of liquid milk and less for manufacture. The new plants, including cheese, were grossly under-utilised and investment virtually ceased.

There was thus little for the Cheese Consortium to do in Britain. Eventually, as a result of Bijlenga being taken over by Alfa-Laval, it was disbanded.

In contrast to the dairy, brewery sales were increasing again. Most of these were for normal vessels and automation but there was one important new trend becoming evident.

'Heavy' brewing, in which wort is fermented at much higher gravity than normal and the resultant beer diluted back to the required strength with pure water, offers substantial economic advantages in reduced size of plant, smaller losses and flexibility. It requires, however, water of very low oxygen content in large quantities for dilution.

A process and plant to provide this was worked out by the A.P.V. Company Inc. in the United States where heavy brewing was first practised. The information was fed back to Crawley and it is now a permanent and growing feature of brewery technology in Britain.

One part of the business which had been steadily growing was that of valves and fittings. The total value was now something over £4 million a year and their production dominated the machine shop.

If 1974 was a difficult year, 1975 was worse. The world suffered an economic recession deeper than any experienced since the war. Industrial production and trade in manufactured goods fell. Most industries found themselves with excess capacity and investment programmes were cut back or deferred. Many of APV's markets were depressed throughout the year as a result.

Nevertheless, due to a substantial backlog at the start, the APV Company was able to have a good year for invoiced sales and profit. The incoming orders, however, showed some reduction in real terms so that the load on the shops fell away towards the end of the year and some redundancies became necessary.

As so often before, the wide spread of interests, both industrially and geographically, proved of great benefit. While the UK dairy order intake continued to go down, the brewery increased again and more than compensated. The fall in value of the pound abroad also meant that foreign earnings were converted at a more favourable rate.

It thus became easier to provide working capital in spite of inflation. In this the company was helped by the new stock relief provisions for taxation. The Board was therefore able to continue its policy of high capital expenditure on new equipment and some very sophisticated and costly machines were installed to reduce production costs.

Towards the end of the year orders for three more large computer-controlled plants were laid. One, for over £3 million, the largest ever laid with APV at that time, was for equipping and automating a new brewery at Gateshead for the Northern Clubs' Federation Brewery Ltd. These three contracts brought the total of computer-controlled process plants in the food industries ordered from APV to twenty-seven.

The company's leading position in this market was recognised by the grant of a Queen's Award for Technological Achievement in 1976 for the application of computer control to beverage and liquid food processing.

The last full year of Peter Seligman's chairmanship was 1976. So it was fitting that it and the early months of 1977 were a time of increasing success when a number of the developments with which he had been associated came to fruition.

The company entered the year with the shops underloaded, with both workforce and staff morale undermined by the Government's pay policies aimed at controlling inflation. Junior management and shop floor supervisory staff were particularly badly affected, as they were everywhere else in the country, and found the differential between their pay and that of the men they were expected to supervise eroded practically to vanishing point. Moreover, markets, with few exceptions, remained depressed all over the world although they improved somewhat in the following year.

It was, therefore, much to the credit of the company that, although there was no increase in turnover, there was a marked increase in profit due to improvements in overall efficiency. That this could be achieved was largely due to the UK brewing industry where the rapid increase in the demand for lager beers led to several new breweries being laid down. The home brewery business that had started to surge up in 1975 therefore continued at a high level in 1976 and even higher thereafter, with the result that Crawley's fabrication capacity became committed for a long period ahead.

The fully automated Toni dairy was put on stream in early 1977. It was undoubtedly the most remarkable achievement of the APV Group in the dairy industry and probably the most comprehensive and complex milk plant in the world. It could handle 220,000 gallons of milk a day to produce pasteurised, UHT and flavoured milks, cream, yogurt, ice-cream and dried milk and whey powders, in all 160 products. As a result of fully automatic process and inventory control, it could be run by only three men per shift (Illustrations 28 and 29).

Automation continued to play a large part in many of the major orders gained. APV had gone a long way since it first installed its own design of computer, combined with its own computer language, operating a 'Highway' system at Scottish & Newcastle in Edinburgh ten years before. The new system, called ACCOS (APV Computer Controlled System) and using a commercial mini computer or, for simpler installations, a microprocessor, had in no way altered the basic principles but the hardware had been considerably refined and, as a result of wide expereience, the software had been vastly developed. Not that it had become incomprehensible to the normal man; on the contrary, it removed the mystique surrounding computer control and allowed the operator to understand the logic of the system.

Big advances were made with industrial plate heat exchangers. The R235, the largest plate heat exchanger yet made anywhere, was shown at the Achema for the first time in June 1976 (Illustration 30). Its development was much assisted by experience with the R405 and 145 but, even so, it needed nearly a couple of years of intensive effort. All this was carried on in complete secrecy and it took competitors completely by surprise. This gigantic machine, with its capability of handling half a million gallons an hour, was aimed at cooling by sea-water, particularly on oil rigs and process plants on estuaries, and at applications in power stations, atomic energy, iron and steel plants and for large effluent duties.

A medium-sized general purpose heat exchanger of the new range, the R8, was also put on the market in mid-1977.

There was an encouraging demand for the new falling film plate evaporator. To go with it, a novel essence recovery system, applicable to citrus as well as soft fruit juices, was developed.

In the meantime, the original climbing and falling film plate evaporator continued to sell well, in spite of competition from falling film tubular machines, and in mid-1976 the thousandth installation was sold, production thus averaging more than one a week since it was first introduced nearly twenty years before.

Towards the end of 1976 occurred an event that cannot be passed over though it does not strictly fall within the purview of this chronicle. In November, Hall-Thermotank joined APV Holdings. The acquisition created a group with a turnover of over £200 million a year. Hall-Thermotank was itself an international organisation with a turnover comparable to that of APV Holdings, a world leader in the application of refrigeration to food processing and in the manufacture of compressors and auxiliary equipment. It was a fitting complement to the existing fields of interest for APV.

The acquisition had no immediate direct effect on The A.P.V. Company Limited but as a result of it, combined with Peter Seligman's retirement, there were big changes in both the Holdings and APV Company Boards.

Sir Iain Stewart, Hall-Thermotank's non-executive Chairman, and D. K. ('Ken') Fraser, their Chief Executive, joined the Holdings Board.

Consequent on Peter Seligman's retirement, Peter Benson became Chairman and Ken Miller a Managing Director of APV Holdings. David Shore and Ken Grover joined the Board, and Madron Seligman became group Marketing Director.

236

On the APV Company Board, Peter Benson became Chairman, Ken Miller, Deputy Chairman, David Shore, Managing Director, and Arthur Boyce, Deputy Managing Director. Charles Brissenden resigned his seat on secondment to the Food and Agricultural Office of the United Nations in India. Bill de Ruyter had been elected to the Board at the beginning of the year to represent the interests of the overseas companies. Now Freddie Cooper, Norman Garrett and Derek Slater were brought in as Overseas, Home Sales and Research Directors respectively.

This story now reaches its last act. At the Annual General Meeting on 18 May 1977, Peter Seligman resigned the chairmanship. Once again, a change of Chairman coincided with the start of a new stage in the history of the company. The acquisition of Hall-Thermotank and the effect of North Sea oil on the value of the pound were bound to have unforeseeable effects.

But, equally, it signalled the end of another. For APV's entire life, over two-thirds of a century, a Seligman, father or son, had been either Chairman or Managing Director of The A.P.V. Company Ltd. This in itself is remarkable, let alone the growth in size of the firm and change in type of the business.

The basic philosophy of the company – to serve equally its customers, its employees, its shareholders and the community because this was the best way to benefit each separately – remained unchanged, too. It was a philosophy that Peter Seligman had done much to develop and it was one that Peter Benson, who had worked so closely with him, was well fitted to carry on. One an engineer, the other an accountant, they mutually respected the other's qualities and together made an excellent team. Seligman had inherited a sound family tradition; Benson had brought a new sense of financial control and its value into the company but he, too, had an instinctive feel for good engineering and scientific innovation. They, and the APV Board with them, had never been reluctant to back innovation with money, provided the risks had been counted, nor had they been critical of failure (as opposed to incompetence or poor management), taking it as one of the necessary risks of an entrepreneurial policy. They had been rewarded with success at a time when it had to be hardly bought.

But the last, characteristically modest, word must rest with Peter Seligman himself. His Chairman's statement, presented on the day of his retirement, concluded:

'I have greatly enjoyed my forty-one years' service to APV. In that time we have seen growth from a small family company to a substantial organisation which has made a real impact on the capital goods industry; as a multi-national group, we can be proud to have made a significant contribution, not only to the economy of this country but to technological progress in many industries throughout the world. Any measure of success I have had in helping with the healthy growth of APV is entirely due to my good fortune in collecting around me in the UK and overseas such an admirable team of loyal and capable people.

'In Peter Benson, the group is fortunate to have a man of such ability ready to take over. I have every confidence that, under his leadership, APV will go from strength to strength in the years ahead.'

# Index

239

# Index

plate evaporator, 58, 154
copper welding, 59
J. W. Wilson, relations with, 38f, 43, 45, 65f, 110ff
stainless steel for food plant, 69f, 71f, 74f, 77ff
HTST pasteurisation process, 102
labour relations and social schemes, 108f, 112, 143, 173
foundry policy, 166f
death, 228
Separator, A. B., see Alfa-Laval
Shanahan, J. B., 209
Shepheard, E. A., 49, 55f, 63
Shore, D. T., 143, 157, 160f, 193, 196f, 218, 221, 236f
Silkeborg, 89
Slater, D., 237
Smith, E. L., 101, 133, 135, 138f, 166, 171
Société APV S.A., 136, 208
Society of Dairy Technology, 128, 144
Soft drinks (see also Fruit juice), deaeration and carbonation, 202
Solvent products, 82
Sommer, Heinrich, Nachfolger, 61, 132
South Africa, 57, 227
Spain, 85, 88, 208f
sales to, 198, 208f, 219
Spencer, Chapman and Messel Limited, 2
Spiro-Gills Limited, 191f
Spray Dryers (see also Anhydro; Fischer), 161, 203
sales of, 161f, 163, 214, 230f
Staff (see also Employees; Engineering; Marketing; Research and Development; Sales; Works), 11, 42f, 88, 93, 97
salaries and bonus, 11f, 23, 33, 39, 68, 93, 110, 112, 118, 145, 178, 189, 234
pensions, 68, 93
redundancies, 174, 179
staff advisory committee, 112, 145, 184
canteen, 113, 148
Stainless steel (see also APV-Paramount; Plate heat exchangers; Works), 69ff, 71f, 77, 122, 126, 128, 149, 164, 223
welding and fabrication, 69f, 75, 126f, 128, 159f, 203f
corrosion, 69f, 75, 122f, 136f
casting, 71, 108, 115f, 134f, 166f, 203f
Stainless Steel Plant Limited, 185f, 187, 188f, 190f, 192
Stanley, E., 27, 33, 42, 133
Stewart, Sir Iain, 236

Sulzer, Gebrüder, 219f
Sweden (see also Alfa-Laval), 79, 122, 186
marketing in, 64, 79, 80, 88, 107, 136, 169, 186, 204
Swedish Farmers' Association (see also Wedholm's), 88, 107
Sweeten, J. L., 205f
Switzerland (see also Autogene Aluminium Schweissung; Seligman, Dr R.), 85, 201, 219f
marketing and sales in, 214, 232, 235

Talman, family, 34f, 68
Tanks (see also Aircraft tanks; Fermenting vessels; Methane (LNG); Transport tanks), breweries, for, 9f, 10f, 16f, 19, 43, 128, 164, 229
dairies, for, 43f, 56f, 77
silo tanks, 223
Tarbet, W. G., 46f, 52f, 54f, 63, 77
Tebel (see also Cheese production), 225, 227, 230, 233
Tetrapak, 200f
Thomas, R., 64, 89, 107, 127, 135
Transport tanks, 26, 43, 44, 61, 85, 133, 166
sales, 61, 85, 133, 166f
production, 89, 92
Tuborg breweries, 129

Ultra high temperature heating (see also Aseptic filling; Automation; Pasteurisation), 124, 152, 155, 172, 200f, 214, 217f, 227
plant for, 124, 152f, 155, 195, 199, 200f, 219f
sales and installations, 172, 201, 204, 211, 227, 235
UNICEF, 127
United Coke and Chemicals, Orgreave, 95, 98
United Dairies (see also Dairy industry), 49, 55, 105
United States (see also Seligman, Dr R.; Walker-Wallace; York), 1, 6f, 45f, 229, 233
marketing in, 56, 63, 65, 71, 86f, 105, 109, 137, 158, 169f, 195, 209, 213f, 229
sales and installations, 71, 80, 105, 170, 196, 209, 219, 226, 230, 232, 233
United States Zinc Company, 7
United Steel Companies (see Appleby-Frodingham; United Coke and Chemicals)

246